GCSE
Combined Science
Physics

Physics is a big part of GCSE Combined Science... and it's not easy. But CGP are on the case — this brilliant book explains everything you'll need to learn!

We've also included plenty of exam-style practice for every section *and* a full set of Physics practice papers so that you can put your new-found knowledge to the test.

What's more, there are step-by-step answers at the back, so you can easily check your work and find out how to pick up any marks you missed out on!

Complete
Revision & Practice
Everything you need to pass the exams!

Contents

Throughout this book you'll see grade stamps like these:

These grade stamps help to show how difficult the questions are.

Remember — to get a top grade you need to be able to answer **all** the questions, not just the hardest ones.

In the real exams, some questions test how well you can structure an answer (as well as your scientific knowledge). In this book, we've marked these questions with an asterisk (*).

Published by CGP

From original material by Richard Parsons.

Editors: Sarah Armstrong, Emily Garrett, Duncan Lindsay, Frances Rooney, Ethan Starmer-Jones, Stephen Walters and Sarah Williams.

Contributors: Paddy Gannon, Barbara Mascetti.

With thanks to Chris Lindle for the proofreading.

With thanks to Jan Greenway for the copyright research.

ISBN: 978 1 78294 879 7

Printed by Elanders Ltd, Newcastle upon Tyne.

Clipart from Corel®

What to Expect in the Exams

Before you get cracking with your revision and exam practice, here's a handy guide to what you'll have to face in the exams — and the special features of this book that we've included especially to help you. You're welcome.

1. **Sections** are Covered in **Different Papers**

For GCSE Combined Science, you'll sit six exam papers at the end of your course, including two physics exams.

Paper	Time	No. of marks	Sections Assessed
Physics 1	1 hr 10 mins	60	1, 2, 3 and 4
Physics 2	1 hr 10 mins	60	5, 6, 7 and 8

2. There are **Different Question Types**

In each exam, you'll be expected to answer a mixture of multiple-choice questions, calculations, short answer questions, and one longer, open response question.

We've marked open response questions in this book with an asterisk (*).

For open response questions, you'll be marked on the structure of your answer, not just its scientific content. So...

Always make sure:
- Your answer is clear and has a logical structure.
- The points you make link together and form a sensible line of reasoning (if appropriate for the question).
- You include detailed, relevant information.

Fortunately, we've included loads of questions in this book, as well as a set of practice papers to give you the best possible preparation for the exams.

3. You'll be Tested on Your **Maths...**

At least 20% of the total marks for GCSE Combined Science will come from questions that test your maths skills. For these questions, always remember to:

EXAMPLE:

Look out for these worked examples in this book — they show you maths skills you'll need in the exam.

- Show your working — you could get marks for this, even if your final answer's wrong.

- Check that you're using the right units.

- Make sure your answer is given to an appropriate number of significant figures.

4. ...and on Your **Practical Skills**

Whenever one of the core practicals crops up in this book, it's marked up with stamps like these...

...and there's a whole section on Practical Skills on pages 137-140.

- GCSE Combined Science contains 18 mandatory core practicals that you'll do during the course. The 7 physics practicals are covered in this book. You can be asked about these, and the practical skills involved in them, in the exams.

- At least 15% of the total marks will be for questions that test your understanding of the practical activities and practical skills.

- For example, you might be asked to comment on the design of an experiment (the apparatus and method), make predictions, analyse or interpret results... Pretty much anything to do with planning and carrying out the investigations.

5. You'll Need to Know About **Working Scientifically**

Working Scientifically is all about how science is applied in the outside world by real scientists.

For example, you might be asked about ways that scientists communicate an idea to get their point across without being biased, or about the limitations of a scientific theory.

Working Scientifically is covered on pages 2-17.

You need to think about the situation that you've been given and use all your scientific savvy to answer the question. Always read the question and any data you've been given really carefully before you start writing your answer.

Working Scientifically

The Scientific Method

This section isn't about how to 'do' science — but it does show you the way most scientists work.

Scientists Come Up With Hypotheses — Then Test Them

1) Scientists try to explain things. They start by observing something they don't understand.

2) They then come up with a hypothesis — a possible explanation for what they've observed.

3) The next step is to test whether the hypothesis might be right or not. This involves making a prediction based on the hypothesis and testing it by gathering evidence (i.e. data) from investigations. If evidence from experiments backs up a prediction, you're a step closer to figuring out if the hypothesis is true.

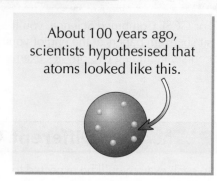

About 100 years ago, scientists hypothesised that atoms looked like this.

Several Scientists Will Test a Hypothesis

1) Normally, scientists share their findings in peer-reviewed journals, or at conferences.

2) Peer-review is where other scientists check results and scientific explanations to make sure they're 'scientific' (e.g. that experiments have been done in a sensible way) before they're published. It helps to detect false claims, but it doesn't mean that findings are correct — just that they're not wrong in any obvious way.

3) Once other scientists have found out about a hypothesis, they'll start basing their own predictions on it and carry out their own experiments. They'll also try to reproduce the original experiments to check the results — and if all the experiments in the world back up the hypothesis, then scientists start to think the hypothesis is true.

4) However, if a scientist does an experiment that doesn't fit with the hypothesis (and other scientists can reproduce the results) then the hypothesis may need to be modified or scrapped altogether.

After more evidence was gathered, scientists changed their hypothesis to this.

If All the Evidence Supports a Hypothesis, It's Accepted — For Now

1) Accepted hypotheses are often referred to as theories. Our currently accepted theories are the ones that have survived this 'trial by evidence' — they've been tested many times over the years and survived.

2) However, theories never become totally indisputable fact. If new evidence comes along that can't be explained using the existing theory, then the hypothesising and testing is likely to start all over again.

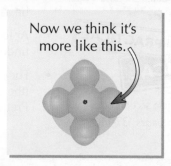

Now we think it's more like this.

Scientific models are constantly being refined...

The scientific method has been developed over time. Aristotle (a Greek philosopher) was the first person to realise that theories need to be based on observations. Muslim scholars then introduced the ideas of creating a hypothesis, testing it, and repeating work to check results.

Models and Communication

Once scientists have made a new discovery, they don't just keep it to themselves. Oh no. Time to learn about how scientific discoveries are communicated, and the models that are used to represent theories.

Theories Can Involve Different Types of Models

1) A representational model is a simplified description or picture of what's going on in real life. Like all models, it can be used to explain observations and make predictions. E.g. the Bohr model of an atom is a simplified way of showing the arrangement of electrons in an atom (see p.71-73). It can be used to explain electron excitations in atoms.

Scientists test models by carrying out experiments to check that the predictions made by the model happen as expected.

2) Computational models use computers to make simulations of complex real-life processes, such as climate change. They're used when there are a lot of different variables (factors that change) to consider, and because you can easily change their design to take into account new data.

3) All models have limitations on what they can explain or predict. E.g. the Bohr model can only be used to make predictions about the electromagnetic radiation emitted by some atoms (like hydrogen).

Scientific Discoveries are Communicated to the General Public

Some scientific discoveries show that people should change their habits, or they might provide ideas that could be developed into new technology. So scientists need to tell the world about their discoveries.

Radioactive materials are used widely in medicine for imaging and treatment. Information about these materials needs to be communicated to doctors so they can make use of them, and to patients, so they can make informed decisions about their treatment.

Scientific Evidence can be Presented in a Biased Way

1) Scientific discoveries that are reported in the media (e.g. newspapers or television) aren't peer-reviewed.

2) This means that, even though news stories are often based on data that has been peer-reviewed, the data might be presented in a way that is over-simplified or inaccurate, making it open to misinterpretation.

3) People who want to make a point can sometimes present data in a biased way (sometimes without knowing they're doing it). For example, a scientist might overemphasise a relationship in the data, or a newspaper article might describe details of data supporting an idea without giving any evidence against it.

Companies can present biased data to help sell products...

Sometimes a company may only want you to see half of the story so they present the data in a biased way. For example, a pharmaceutical company may want to encourage you to buy their drugs by telling you about all the positives, but not report the results of any unfavourable studies.

Issues Created by Science

Science has helped us make progress in loads of areas, from advances in medicine to space travel. But science still has its issues. And it can't answer everything, as you're about to find out.

Scientific Developments are Great, but they can Raise Issues

Scientific knowledge is increased by doing experiments. And this knowledge leads to scientific developments, e.g. new technologies or new advice. These developments can create issues though. For example:

> Economic issues: Society can't always afford to do things scientists recommend (e.g. investing in alternative energy sources) without cutting back elsewhere.

> Social issues: Decisions based on scientific evidence affect people — e.g. should fossil fuels be taxed more highly? Would the effect on people's lifestyles be acceptable?

> Personal issues: Some decisions will affect individuals. For example, someone might support alternative energy, but object if a wind farm was built next to their house.

> Environmental issues: Human activity often affects the natural environment. For example, building a dam to produce electricity will change the local habitat so some species might be displaced. But it will also reduce our need for fossil fuels, so will help to reduce climate change.

Science Can't Answer Every Question — Especially Ethical Ones

1) We don't understand everything. We're always finding out more, but we'll never know all the answers.

2) In order to answer scientific questions, scientists need data to provide evidence for their hypotheses.

3) Some questions can't be answered yet because the data can't currently be collected, or because there's not enough data to support a theory.

4) Eventually, as we get more evidence, we'll answer some of the questions that currently can't be answered, e.g. what the impact of global warming on sea levels will be. But there will always be the "Should we be doing this at all?"-type questions that experiments can't help us to answer...

> Think about new drugs which can be taken to boost your 'brain power'.
> - Some people think they're good as they could improve concentration or memory. New drugs could let people think in ways beyond the powers of normal brains.
> - Other people say they're bad — they could give some people an unfair advantage in exams. And people might be pressured into taking them so that they could work more effectively, and for longer hours.

There are often issues with new scientific developments...

The trouble is, there's often no clear right answer where these issues are concerned. Different people have different views, depending on their priorities. These issues are full of grey areas.

Risk

Scientific discoveries are often great, but they can prove risky. With dangers all around, you've got to be aware of hazards — this includes how likely they are to cause harm and how serious the effects may be.

Nothing is Completely Risk-Free

1) A hazard is something that could potentially cause harm.

2) All hazards have a risk attached to them — this is the chance that the hazard will cause harm.

3) The risks of some things seem pretty obvious, or we've known about them for a while, like the risk of causing acid rain by polluting the atmosphere, or of having a car accident when you're travelling in a car.

4) New technology arising from scientific advances can bring new risks, e.g. scientists are unsure whether nanoparticles that are being used in cosmetics and suncream might be harming the cells in our bodies. These risks need to be considered alongside the benefits of the technology, e.g. improved sun protection.

5) You can estimate the size of a risk based on how many times something happens in a big sample (e.g. 100 000 people) over a given period (e.g. a year). For example, you could assess the risk of a driver crashing by recording how many people in a group of 100 000 drivers crashed their cars over a year.

6) To make decisions about activities that involve hazards, we need to take into account the chance of the hazard causing harm, and how serious the consequences would be if it did. If an activity involves a hazard that's very likely to cause harm, with serious consequences if it does, it's considered high-risk.

People Make Their Own Decisions About Risk

1) Not all risks have the same consequences, e.g. if you chop veg with a sharp knife you risk cutting your finger, but if you go scuba-diving you risk death. You're much more likely to cut your finger during half an hour of chopping than to die during half an hour of scuba-diving. But most people are happier to accept a higher probability of an accident if the consequences are short-lived and fairly minor.

2) People tend to be more willing to accept a risk if they choose to do something (e.g. go scuba diving), compared to having the risk imposed on them (e.g. having a nuclear power station built next door).

3) People's perception of risk (how risky they think something is) isn't always accurate. They tend to view familiar activities as low-risk and unfamiliar activities as high-risk — even if that's not the case. For example, cycling on roads is often high-risk, but many people are happy to do it because it's a familiar activity. Air travel is actually pretty safe, but a lot of people perceive it as high-risk.

4) People may over-estimate the risk of things with long-term or invisible effects, e.g. ionising radiation.

The pros and cons of new technology must be weighed up...

The world's a dangerous place and it's impossible to rule out the chance of an accident altogether. But if you can recognise hazards and take steps to reduce the risks, you're more likely to stay safe.

Designing Investigations

Dig out your lab coat and dust off your badly-scratched safety goggles... it's <u>investigation time</u>.

Evidence Can Support or Disprove a Hypothesis

1) Scientists <u>observe</u> things and come up with <u>hypotheses</u> to explain them (see p.2). You need to be able to do the same. For example:

> <u>Observation</u>: People with big feet have spots. <u>Hypothesis</u>: Having big feet causes spots.

2) To <u>determine</u> whether or not a hypothesis is <u>right</u>, you need to do an <u>investigation</u> to gather evidence. To do this, you need to use your hypothesis to make a <u>prediction</u> — something you think <u>will happen</u> that you can test. E.g. people who have bigger feet will have more spots.

Investigations include experiments and studies.

3) Investigations are used to see if there are <u>patterns</u> or <u>relationships</u> between <u>two variables</u>, e.g. to see if there's a pattern or relationship between the variables 'number of spots' and 'size of feet'.

Evidence Needs to be Repeatable, Reproducible and Valid

1) <u>Repeatable</u> means that if the <u>same person</u> does an experiment again using the <u>same methods</u> and equipment, they'll get <u>similar results</u>.

2) <u>Reproducible</u> means that if <u>someone else</u> does the experiment, or a <u>different</u> method or piece of equipment is used, the results will still be <u>similar</u>.

3) If data is <u>repeatable</u> and <u>reproducible</u>, it's <u>reliable</u> and scientists are more likely to <u>have confidence</u> in it.

4) <u>Valid results</u> are both repeatable and reproducible AND they <u>answer the original question</u>. They come from experiments that were designed to be a <u>FAIR TEST</u>...

Make an Investigation a Fair Test By Controlling the Variables

1) In a lab experiment you usually <u>change one variable</u> and <u>measure</u> how it affects <u>another variable</u>.

2) To make it a fair test, <u>everything else</u> that could affect the results should <u>stay the same</u> — otherwise you can't tell if the thing you're changing is causing the results or not.

3) The variable you <u>CHANGE</u> is called the <u>INDEPENDENT</u> variable.

4) The variable you <u>MEASURE</u> when you change the independent variable is the <u>DEPENDENT</u> variable.

5) The variables that you <u>KEEP THE SAME</u> are called <u>CONTROL</u> variables.

> You could find how <u>current</u> through a circuit component affects the <u>potential difference</u> <u>(p.d.)</u> across the component by measuring the <u>potential difference</u> at different currents. The <u>independent variable</u> is the <u>current</u>. The <u>dependent variable</u> is the <u>potential difference</u>. <u>Control variables</u> include the <u>temperature</u> of the component, the <u>p.d.</u> of the power supply, etc.

6) Because you can't always control all the variables, you often need to use a <u>control experiment</u>. This is an experiment that's kept under the <u>same conditions</u> as the rest of the investigation, but <u>doesn't</u> have anything <u>done</u> to it. This is so that you can see what happens when you don't change anything at all.

Designing Investigations

The **Bigger** the **Sample Size** the **Better**

1) Data based on <u>small samples</u> isn't as good as data based on large samples. A sample should <u>represent</u> the <u>whole population</u> (i.e. it should share as many of the characteristics in the population as possible) — a small sample can't do that as well. It's also harder to spot <u>anomalies</u> if your sample size is too small.

2) The <u>bigger</u> the sample size the <u>better</u>, but scientists have to be <u>realistic</u> when choosing how big. For example, if you were studying the effects of <u>living</u> near a <u>nuclear power plant</u>, it'd be great to study <u>everyone</u> who lived near a nuclear power plant (a huge sample), but it'd take ages and cost a bomb. It's more realistic to study a thousand people, with a range of ages and races and across both genders.

Your **Equipment** has to be **Right for the Job**

1) The measuring equipment you use has to be <u>sensitive enough</u> to measure the changes you're looking for. For example, if you need to measure changes of 1 cm³ you need to use a <u>measuring cylinder</u> that can measure in <u>1 cm³</u> steps — it'd be no good trying with one that only measures 10 cm³ steps.

2) The <u>smallest change</u> a measuring instrument can <u>detect</u> is called its <u>resolution</u>. E.g. some mass balances have a resolution of 1 g, some have a resolution of 0.1 g, and some are even more sensitive.

3) Also, equipment needs to be <u>calibrated</u> by measuring a known value. If there's a <u>difference</u> between the <u>measured</u> and <u>known value</u>, you can use this to <u>correct</u> the inaccuracy of the equipment.

Data Should be **Repeatable, Reproducible, Accurate** and **Precise**

1) To <u>check repeatability</u> you need to <u>repeat</u> the readings and check that the results are similar. You need to repeat each reading at least <u>three times</u>.

2) To make sure your results are <u>reproducible</u> you can cross check them by taking a <u>second set of readings</u> with <u>another instrument</u> (or a <u>different observer</u>).

3) Your data also needs to be <u>accurate</u>. Really accurate results are those that are <u>really close</u> to the <u>true answer</u>. The accuracy of your results usually depends on your <u>method</u> — you need to make sure you're measuring the right thing and that you don't <u>miss anything</u> that should be included in the measurements. E.g. estimating the <u>volume</u> of an irregularly shaped solid by <u>measuring the sides</u> isn't very accurate because this will not take into account any gaps in the object. It's <u>more accurate</u> to measure the volume using a <u>eureka can</u> (see p.123).

4) Your data also needs to be <u>precise</u>. Precise results are ones where the data is <u>all really close</u> to the <u>mean</u> (average) of your repeated results (i.e. not spread out).

Repeat	Data set 1	Data set 2
1	12	11
2	14	17
3	13	14
Mean	<u>13</u>	<u>14</u>

Data set 1 is more precise than data set 2.

Designing Investigations

You Need to Look out for **Errors** and **Anomalous Results**

1) The results of your experiment will always <u>vary a bit</u> because of <u>random errors</u> — unpredictable differences caused by things like <u>human errors</u> in <u>measuring</u>. The errors when you make a reading from a ruler are random. You have to estimate or round the distance when it's between two marks — so sometimes your figure will be a bit above the real one, and sometimes it will be a bit below.

2) You can <u>reduce</u> the effect of random errors by taking <u>repeat readings</u> and finding the <u>mean</u>. This will make your results <u>more precise</u>.

If there's no systematic error, then doing repeats and calculating a mean can make your results more accurate.

3) If a measurement is wrong by the <u>same amount every time</u>, it's called a <u>systematic error</u>. For example, if you measured from the very end of your ruler instead of from the 0 cm mark every time, all your measurements would be a bit small. Repeating the experiment in the exact same way and calculating a mean <u>won't</u> correct a systematic error.

4) Just to make things more complicated, if a systematic error is caused by using <u>equipment</u> that <u>isn't zeroed properly</u>, it's called a <u>zero error</u>. For example, if a mass balance always reads 1 gram before you put anything on it, all your measurements will be 1 gram too heavy.

5) You can <u>compensate</u> for some systematic errors if you know about them, e.g. if a mass balance always reads 1 gram before you put anything on it, you can subtract 1 gram from all your results.

6) Sometimes you get a result that <u>doesn't fit in</u> with the rest at all. This is called an <u>anomalous result</u>. You should investigate it and try to <u>work out what happened</u>. If you can work out what happened (e.g. you measured something wrong) you can <u>ignore</u> it when processing your results.

Investigations Can be **Hazardous**

1) <u>Hazards</u> from science experiments might include:

- <u>Lasers</u>, e.g. if a laser is directed into the eye, this can cause blindness.
- <u>Gamma radiation</u>, e.g. gamma-emitting radioactive sources can cause cancer.
- <u>Fire</u>, e.g. an unattended Bunsen burner is a fire hazard.
- <u>Electricity</u>, e.g. faulty electrical equipment could give you a shock.

You can find out about potential hazards by looking in textbooks, doing some internet research, or asking your teacher.

2) Part of planning an investigation is making sure that it's <u>safe</u>.

3) You should always make sure that you <u>identify</u> all the hazards that you might encounter. Then you should think of ways of <u>reducing the risks</u> from the hazards you've identified. For example:

- If you're working with <u>springs</u>, always wear safety goggles. This will reduce the risk of the spring hitting your eye if the spring snaps.
- If you're using a <u>Bunsen burner</u>, stand it on a heat proof mat to reduce the risk of starting a fire.

Designing an investigation is an involved process...

<u>Collecting data</u> is what investigations are all about. Designing a good investigation is really important to make sure that any data collected is <u>accurate</u>, <u>precise</u>, <u>repeatable</u> and <u>reproducible</u>.

Processing Data

Processing your data means doing some <u>calculations</u> with it to make it <u>more useful</u>.

Data Needs to be Organised

1) Tables are really useful for <u>organising data</u>.
2) When you draw a table <u>use a ruler</u> and make sure <u>each column</u> has a <u>heading</u> (including the <u>units</u>).

There are Different Ways to Process Your Data

1) When you've done repeats of an experiment you should always calculate the <u>mean</u> (average). To do this <u>add together</u> all the data values and <u>divide</u> by the total number of values in the sample.
2) You can also find the <u>mode</u> of your results — this is the <u>value</u> that <u>occurs</u> the <u>most</u> in your set of results.
3) The <u>median</u> can be found by writing your results in numerical <u>order</u> — the median is the <u>middle number</u>.

Ignore anomalous results when calculating the mean, mode and median.

 **EXAMPLE:** **The results of an experiment show the extension of two springs when a force is applied to both of them. Calculate the mean, mode and median of the extension for both springs.**

Spring	Repeat (cm)					Mean (cm)	Mode (cm)	Median (cm)
	1	2	3	4	5			
A	18	26	22	26	28	(18 + 26 + 22 + 26 + 28) ÷ 5 = 24	26	26
B	11	14	20	15	20	(11 + 14 + 20 + 15 + 20) ÷ 5 = 16	20	15

Round to the Lowest Number of Significant Figures

The <u>first significant figure</u> of a number is the first digit that's <u>not zero</u>. The second and third significant figures come <u>straight after</u> (even if they're zeros). You should be aware of significant figures in calculations.

1) In <u>any</u> calculation, you should round the answer to the <u>lowest number of significant figures</u> (s.f.) given.
2) Remember to write down <u>how many</u> significant figures you've rounded to after your answer.
3) If your calculation has multiple steps, <u>only</u> round the <u>final</u> answer, or it won't be as accurate.

 **EXAMPLE:** **The mass of a solid is 0.24 g and its volume is 0.715 cm³. Calculate the density of the solid.**

Density = 0.24 g ÷ 0.715 cm³ = 0.33566... = 0.34 g/cm³ (2 s.f.)

          2 s.f.   3 s.f.   Final answer should be rounded to 2 s.f.

 EXAM TIP

Don't forget your calculator...

In the exam you could be given some <u>data</u> and be expected to <u>process it</u> in some way. Make sure you keep an eye on <u>significant figures</u> in your answers and <u>always write down your working</u>.

Presenting Data

Once you've processed your data, e.g. by calculating the mean, you can present your results in a nice <u>chart</u> or <u>graph</u>. This will help you to <u>spot any patterns</u> in your data.

Bar Charts Can be Used to Show **Different Types** of **Data**

Bar charts can be used to display:

1) <u>Categoric</u> data (comes in distinct categories, e.g. states of matter, types of nuclear radiation).

2) <u>Discrete</u> data (the data can be counted in chunks, where there's no in-between value, e.g. number of protons is discrete because you can't have half a proton).

3) <u>Continuous</u> data (numerical data that can have any value in a range, e.g. length or temperature).

There are some <u>golden rules</u> you need to follow for <u>drawing</u> bar charts:

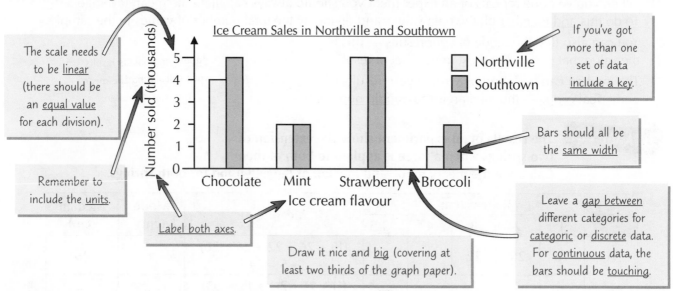

The scale needs to be <u>linear</u> (there should be an <u>equal value</u> for each division).

Remember to include the <u>units</u>.

Label both axes.

Draw it nice and <u>big</u> (covering at least two thirds of the graph paper).

If you've got more than one set of data <u>include a key</u>.

Bars should all be the <u>same width</u>.

Leave a <u>gap between</u> different categories for <u>categoric</u> or <u>discrete</u> data. For <u>continuous</u> data, the bars should be <u>touching</u>.

Graphs can be Used to Plot **Continuous Data**

1) If both variables are <u>continuous</u> you should use a <u>graph</u> to display the data.

2) Here are the <u>rules</u> for plotting points on a graph:

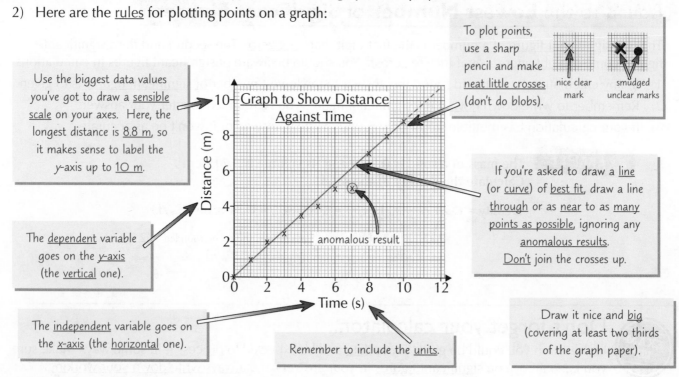

Use the biggest data values you've got to draw a <u>sensible scale</u> on your axes. Here, the longest distance is <u>8.8 m</u>, so it makes sense to label the y-axis up to <u>10 m</u>.

The <u>dependent</u> variable goes on the <u>y-axis</u> (the <u>vertical</u> one).

The <u>independent</u> variable goes on the <u>x-axis</u> (the <u>horizontal</u> one).

Remember to include the <u>units</u>.

To plot points, use a sharp pencil and make <u>neat little crosses</u> (don't do blobs).

nice clear mark

smudged unclear marks

If you're asked to draw a <u>line</u> (or <u>curve</u>) of <u>best fit</u>, draw a line <u>through</u> or as <u>near</u> to as <u>many points as possible</u>, ignoring any <u>anomalous results</u>. <u>Don't</u> join the crosses up.

Draw it nice and <u>big</u> (covering at least two thirds of the graph paper).

More on Graphs

Graphs aren't just fun to plot, they're also really useful for showing <u>trends</u> in your data.

Graphs Can Give You a Lot of Information About Your Data

1) The <u>gradient</u> (slope) of a graph tells you how quickly the <u>dependent variable</u> changes if you change the <u>independent variable</u>.

$$\text{gradient} = \frac{\text{change in } y}{\text{change in } x}$$

You can use this method to calculate other rates from a graph, not just the rate of change of distance (which is speed). Just remember that a rate is how much something changes over time, so x needs to be the time.

This <u>graph</u> shows the <u>distance travelled</u> by a vehicle against <u>time</u>. The graph is <u>linear</u> (it's a straight line graph), so you can simply calculate the <u>gradient</u> of the line to find out the <u>speed</u> of the vehicle.

1) To calculate the gradient, pick <u>two points</u> on the line that are easy to read and a <u>good distance</u> apart.
2) <u>Draw a line down</u> from one of the points and a <u>line across</u> from the other to make a <u>triangle</u>. The line drawn down the side of the triangle is the <u>change in y</u> and the line across the bottom is the <u>change in x</u>.

Change in y = 6.8 – 2.0 = 4.8 m   Change in x = 5.2 – 1.6 = 3.6 s

$$\text{Rate} = \text{gradient} = \frac{\text{change in } y}{\text{change in } x} = \frac{4.8\,\text{m}}{3.6\,\text{s}} = \underline{1.3\ \text{m/s}}$$

The units of the gradient are (units of y)/(units of x).

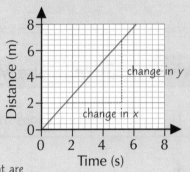

2) To find the <u>gradient of a curve</u> at a <u>certain point</u>, draw a <u>tangent</u> to the curve at that point and then find the <u>gradient of the tangent</u>. See page 22 for details on how to do this.

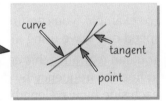

3) The <u>intercept</u> of a graph is where the line of best fit crosses one of the <u>axes</u>. The <u>x-intercept</u> is where the line of best fit crosses the x-axis and the <u>y-intercept</u> is where it crosses the <u>y-axis</u>.

Graphs Show the Relationship Between Two Variables

1) You can get <u>three</u> types of <u>correlation</u> (relationship) between variables:

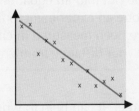

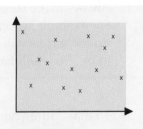

<u>POSITIVE</u> correlation: as one variable <u>increases</u> the other <u>increases</u>.

<u>INVERSE</u> (negative) correlation: as one variable <u>increases</u> the other <u>decreases</u>.

<u>NO</u> correlation: <u>no relationship</u> between the two variables.

2) Just because there's correlation, it doesn't mean the change in one variable is <u>causing</u> the change in the other — there might be <u>other factors</u> involved (see page 15).

Units

Graphs and maths skills are all very well, but the numbers don't mean much if you don't get the <u>units</u> right.

S.I. Units Are Used All Round the World

1) It wouldn't be all that useful if I defined volume in terms of <u>bath tubs</u>, you defined it in terms of <u>egg-cups</u> and my pal Fred defined it in terms of <u>balloons</u> — we'd never be able to compare our data.

2) To stop this happening, scientists have come up with a set of <u>standard units</u>, called S.I. units, that all scientists use to measure their data. Here are some S.I. units you'll see in physics:

Quantity	S.I. Base Unit
mass	kilogram, kg
length	metre, m
time	second, s
temperature	kelvin, K

Always Check The Values Used in Equations Have the Right Units

1) Formulas and equations show <u>relationships</u> between <u>variables</u>.

2) To <u>rearrange</u> an equation, make sure that whatever you do to <u>one side</u> of the equation you also do to the <u>other side</u>.

- For example, you can find the <u>speed</u> of a wave using the equation: ⟹ wave speed = frequency × wavelength
- You can <u>rearrange</u> this equation to find the <u>frequency</u> by <u>dividing</u> <u>each side</u> by wavelength to give: ⟹ frequency = wave speed ÷ wavelength

3) To use a formula, you need to know the values of <u>all but one</u> of the variables. <u>Substitute</u> the values you do know into the formula, and do the calculation to work out the final variable.

4) Always make sure the values you put into an equation or formula have the <u>right units</u>. For example, you might have done an experiment to find the speed of a trolley. The distance the trolley travels will probably have been measured in cm, but the equation to find speed uses distance in m. So you'll have to <u>convert</u> your distance from cm to m before you put it into the equation.

5) To make sure your units are <u>correct</u>, it can help to write down the <u>units</u> on each line of your <u>calculation</u>.

S.I. units help scientists to compare data...

You can only really <u>compare</u> things if they're in the <u>same units</u>. For example, if you measured the speed of one car in m/s, and one in km/h, it would be hard to know which car was going faster.

Converting Units

You can <u>convert units</u> using <u>scaling prefixes</u>. This can save you from having to write a lot of 0's...

Scaling Prefixes Can Be Used for Large and Small Quantities

1) Quantities come in a huge <u>range</u> of sizes. For example, the volume of a swimming pool might be around 2 000 000 000 cm^3, while the volume of a cup is around 250 cm^3.

2) To make the size of numbers more <u>manageable</u>, larger or smaller units are used. These are the <u>S.I. base units</u> (e.g. metres) with a <u>prefix</u> in front:

Prefix	tera (T)	giga (G)	mega (M)	kilo (k)	deci (d)	centi (c)	milli (m)	micro (μ)	nano (n)
Multiple of Unit	10^{12}	10^9	1 000 000 (10^6)	1000	0.1	0.01	0.001	0.000001 (10^{-6})	10^{-9}

3) These <u>prefixes</u> tell you <u>how much bigger</u> or <u>smaller</u> a unit is than the base unit. So one <u>kilo</u>metre is <u>one thousand</u> metres.

4) To <u>swap</u> from one unit to another, all you need to know is what number you have to divide or multiply by to get from the original unit to the new unit — this is called the <u>conversion factor</u>.

The conversion factor is the number of times the smaller unit goes into the larger unit.

- To go from a <u>bigger unit</u> (like m) to a <u>smaller unit</u> (like cm), you <u>multiply</u> by the conversion factor.
- To go from a <u>smaller unit</u> (like g) to a <u>bigger unit</u> (like kg), you <u>divide</u> by the conversion factor.

5) Here are some conversions that'll be useful for physics:

Energy can have units of J and kJ.

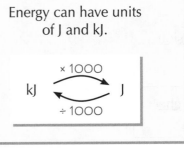

Mass can have units of kg and g.

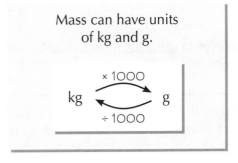

Volume can have units of m^3 and cm^3.

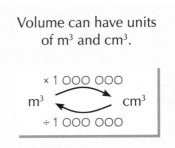

Density can have units of kg/m^3 and g/cm^3.

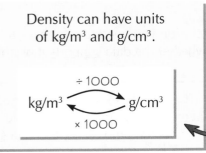

Watch out for conversions involving density — you need to divide when going from kg/m^3 to g/cm^3, not multiply.

6) Numbers can also be written in <u>standard form</u>, e.g. 1×10^2 m = 100 m. Make sure you know how to work with standard form on <u>your calculator</u>.

To convert from bigger units to smaller units...

...multiply by the conversion factor. And to convert from <u>smaller units</u> to <u>bigger units</u>, <u>divide</u> by the <u>conversion factor</u>. Don't go getting this rule muddled up and the wrong way round...

Drawing Conclusions

Once you've designed your experiment, carried it out, processed and presented your data, it's finally time to sit down and work out exactly what your data tells you. Time for some fun with <u>conclusions</u>...

You Can **Only Conclude** What the Data Shows and **No More**

1) Drawing conclusions might seem pretty straightforward — you just <u>look at your data</u> and <u>say what pattern or relationship you see</u> between the dependent and independent variables.

The table on the right shows the potential difference across a light bulb for three <u>different</u> currents through the bulb:

Current (A)	Potential difference (V)
6	4
9	10
12	13

<u>CONCLUSION</u>: A <u>higher current</u> through the bulb gives a higher <u>potential difference</u> across the bulb.

2) But you've got to be really careful that your conclusion <u>matches the data</u> you've got and <u>doesn't go any further</u>.

> You <u>can't</u> conclude that the potential difference across <u>any circuit component</u> will be higher for a larger current — the results might be completely different.

3) You also need to be able to <u>use your results</u> to <u>justify your conclusion</u> (i.e. back up your conclusion with some specific data).

> The potential difference across the bulb was <u>9 V higher</u> with a current of 12 A compared to a current of 6 A.

4) When writing a conclusion you need to <u>refer back</u> to the original hypothesis and say whether the data <u>supports it</u> or not:

> The hypothesis for this experiment might have been that a higher current through the bulb would <u>increase</u> the potential difference across the bulb. If so, the data <u>supports</u> the hypothesis.

You should be able to justify your conclusion with your data...

You should always be able to explain how your data <u>supports</u> your <u>conclusion</u>. It's easy to go too far with conclusions and start making <u>bold claims</u> that your data simply can't back up. When you're drawing conclusions, it's also important that you refer back to your <u>initial hypothesis</u>, the one you made right back at the start of the investigation, to see whether your data supports it or not.

Correlation and Cause

Don't get carried away when you're <u>drawing conclusions</u> — <u>correlation</u> doesn't always mean <u>cause</u>. There could be a few reasons why two variables appear to be linked, as you're about to find out.

Correlation DOES NOT Mean Cause

If two things are correlated (i.e. there's a relationship between them) it <u>doesn't</u> necessarily mean a change in one variable is <u>causing</u> the change in the other — this is <u>REALLY IMPORTANT</u> — <u>DON'T FORGET IT</u>.

There are Three Possible Reasons for a Correlation

1) <u>CHANCE</u>: It might seem strange, but two things can show a correlation purely due to <u>chance</u>.

> For example, one study might find a correlation between people's hair colour and how good they are at frisbee. But other scientists <u>don't</u> get a correlation when they investigate it — the results of the first study are just a <u>fluke</u>.

2) <u>LINKED BY A 3RD VARIABLE</u>: A lot of the time it may <u>look</u> as if a change in one variable is causing a change in the other, but it <u>isn't</u> — a <u>third variable links</u> the two things.

> For example, there's a correlation between <u>water temperature</u> and <u>shark attacks</u>. This isn't because warmer water makes sharks crazy. Instead, they're linked by a third variable — the <u>number of people swimming</u> (more people swim when the water's hotter, and with more people in the water you get more shark attacks).

3) <u>CAUSE</u>: Sometimes a change in one variable does <u>cause</u> a change in the other. You can only conclude that a correlation is due to cause when you've <u>controlled all the variables</u> that could, just could, be affecting the result.

> For example, there's a correlation between <u>smoking</u> and <u>lung cancer</u>. This is because chemicals in tobacco smoke cause lung cancer. This conclusion was only made once <u>other variables</u> (such as age and exposure to other things that cause cancer) had been <u>controlled</u> and shown <u>not</u> to affect people's risk of getting lung cancer.

Two variables could appear to be linked by chance...

<u>Correlation</u> doesn't necessarily mean <u>cause</u> — two variables might appear to be linked but it could just be down to <u>chance</u>, or they could be linked by a <u>third variable</u>. When you draw conclusions, make sure you're not jumping to conclusions about cause, and check that you properly <u>consider</u> all the reasons why two variables might appear to be linked.

Uncertainty

Uncertainty is how sure you can really be about your data. There's a little bit of maths to do, and also a formula to learn. But don't worry too much — it's no more than a simple bit of subtraction and division.

Uncertainty is the Amount of Error Your Measurements Might Have

1) When you repeat a measurement, you often get a slightly different figure each time you do it due to random error. This means that each result has some uncertainty to it.

2) The measurements you make will also have some uncertainty in them due to limits in the resolution of the equipment you use (see page 7).

3) This all means that the mean of a set of results will also have some uncertainty to it. You can calculate the uncertainty of a mean result using the equation:

$$\text{uncertainty} = \frac{\text{range}}{2}$$

The range is the largest value minus the smallest value.

4) The larger the range, the less precise your results are and the more uncertainty there will be in your results. Uncertainties are shown using the '±' symbol.

 EXAMPLE:

The table below shows the results of an experiment to determine the speed of the trolley as it rolls down a ramp. Calculate the uncertainty of the mean.

Repeat	1	2	3	4
Speed (m/s)	2.01	1.98	2.00	2.01

1) First work out the range:

Range = 2.01 − 1.98 = 0.030 m/s

2) Then find the mean:

Mean = (2.01 + 1.98 + 2.00 + 2.01) ÷ 4

= 8.00 ÷ 4 = 2.00

3) Use the range to find the uncertainty:

Uncertainty = range ÷ 2 = 0.030 ÷ 2 = 0.015 m/s

So the uncertainty of the mean = 2.00 ± 0.015 m/s

5) Measuring a greater amount of something helps to reduce uncertainty. For example, in an experiment investigating speed, measuring the distance travelled over a longer period compared to a shorter period will reduce the uncertainty in your results.

 MATHS TIP

The smaller the uncertainty, the more precise your results...

Remember that equation for uncertainty. You never know when you might need it — you could be expected to use it in the exams. You need to make sure all the data is in the same units though. For example, if you had some measurements in metres, and some in centimetres, you'd need to convert them all into either metres or centimetres before you set about calculating uncertainty.

Evaluations

Hurrah! The end of another investigation. Well, now you have to work out all the things you did <u>wrong</u>. That's what <u>evaluations</u> are all about I'm afraid. Best get cracking with this page...

Evaluations — Describe **How** Experiments Could be **Improved**

An evaluation is a <u>critical analysis</u> of the whole investigation.

1) You should comment on the <u>method</u> — was it <u>valid</u>?
   Did you control all the other variables to make it a <u>fair test</u>?

2) Comment on the <u>quality</u> of the <u>results</u> — was there <u>enough evidence</u> to reach a valid <u>conclusion</u>? Were the results <u>repeatable</u>, <u>reproducible</u>, <u>accurate</u> and <u>precise</u>?

3) Were there any <u>anomalous</u> results? If there were <u>none</u> then <u>say so</u>.
   If there were any, try to <u>explain</u> them — were they caused by <u>errors</u> in measurement?
   Were there any other <u>variables</u> that could have <u>affected</u> the results?
   You should comment on the level of <u>uncertainty</u> in your results too.

4) All this analysis will allow you to say how <u>confident</u> you are that your conclusion is <u>right</u>.

5) Then you can suggest any <u>changes</u> to the <u>method</u> that would <u>improve</u> the quality of the results, so that you could have <u>more confidence</u> in your conclusion. For example, you might suggest <u>changing</u> the way you controlled a variable, or <u>increasing</u> the number of <u>measurements</u> you took. Taking more measurements at <u>narrower intervals</u> could give you a <u>more accurate result</u>. For example:

> <u>Springs</u> have an <u>elastic limit</u> (a maximum extension before they stop springing back to their original size). Say you use several <u>identical</u> springs to do an experiment to find the elastic limit of the springs. If you apply forces of 1 N, 2 N, 3 N, 4 N and 5 N, and from the results see that the elastic limit is somewhere <u>between 4 N and 5 N</u>, you could then <u>repeat</u> the experiment with one of the other springs, taking <u>more measurements between 4 N and 5 N</u> to get a <u>more accurate</u> value for the elastic limit.

6) You could also make more <u>predictions</u> based on your conclusion, then <u>further experiments</u> could be carried out to test them.

When suggesting improvements to the investigation, always make sure that you say why you think this would make the results better.

Always look for ways to improve your investigations...

So there you have it — <u>Working Scientifically</u>. Make sure you know this stuff like the back of your hand. It's not just in the lab, when you're carrying out your groundbreaking <u>investigations</u>, that you'll need to know how to work scientifically. You can be asked about it in the <u>exams</u> as well. So swot up...

Scalars and Vectors

There are a lot of very similar <u>variables</u> on this page, but they're <u>different</u> in some <u>very important</u> ways, so prepare to pay extra close attention. It's down to whether they're a <u>vector</u> or a <u>scalar</u> quantity.

Vectors Have **Magnitude** and **Direction**

1) Vector quantities have a <u>magnitude</u> (size) and a <u>direction</u>.

2) Lots of <u>physical quantities</u> are vector quantities:

> <u>Vector quantities</u>: force, velocity, displacement, weight, acceleration, momentum, etc.

3) Some physical quantities <u>only</u> have magnitude and <u>no direction</u>. These are called <u>scalar quantities</u>:

> <u>Scalar quantities</u>: speed, distance, mass, energy, temperature, time, etc.

> <u>Velocity</u> is a <u>vector</u>, but <u>speed</u> is a <u>scalar</u> quantity.
> Both bikes are travelling at the same <u>speed</u>, v.
> They have <u>different velocities</u> because
> they are travelling in different <u>directions</u>.

Distance is **Scalar**, Displacement is a **Vector**

1) <u>Distance</u> is just <u>how far</u> an object has moved. It's a <u>scalar</u> quantity so it doesn't involve <u>direction</u>.

2) Displacement is a <u>vector</u> quantity. It measures the distance and direction in a <u>straight line</u> from an object's <u>starting point</u> to its <u>finishing point</u> — e.g. the plane flew 5 metres <u>north</u>. The direction could be <u>relative to a point</u>, e.g. <u>towards the school</u>, or a <u>bearing</u> (a <u>three-digit angle from north</u>, e.g. <u>035°</u>).

3) If you walk 5 m <u>north</u>, then 5 m <u>south</u>, your <u>displacement</u> is <u>0 m</u> but the <u>distance</u> travelled is <u>10 m</u>.

Speed and **Velocity** are Both **How Fast You're Going**

1) <u>Speed and velocity</u> both measure <u>how fast</u> you're going, but <u>speed</u> is a <u>scalar</u> and <u>velocity</u> is a <u>vector</u>:

> <u>Speed</u> is just <u>how fast</u> you're going (e.g. 30 mph or 20 m/s)
> with no regard to the direction.
> <u>Velocity</u> is speed in a given <u>direction</u>, e.g. 30 mph north or 20 m/s, 060°.

2) This means you can have objects travelling at a <u>constant speed</u> with a <u>changing velocity</u>. This happens when the object is <u>changing direction</u> whilst staying at the <u>same speed</u>.

When it comes to vectors the sign is important...

If you're working on a question which involves <u>vectors</u> that point in <u>opposite directions</u>, pick one direction to have a <u>positive</u> sign and the other <u>negative</u>. For example, if you decide to make all velocities pointing to the left positive, be sure that you give those pointing to the right a negative sign.

Speed

Speed tells you the <u>distance</u> an object travels in a <u>given time</u>. You're typically going to deal with speeds in metres per second — so you need to be able to <u>estimate</u> some everyday speeds in these units.

You Need to Know Some **Typical** Everyday **Speeds**

1) For an object travelling at a <u>constant</u> speed, <u>distance</u>, (average) <u>speed</u> and <u>time</u> are related by the formula:

> **distance travelled (m) = (average) speed (m/s) × time (s)**

2) Objects <u>rarely</u> travel at a <u>constant speed</u>. E.g. when you <u>walk</u>, <u>run</u> or travel in a <u>car</u>, your speed is <u>always changing</u>. Make sure you have an idea of the <u>typical speeds</u> for different transport methods:

> <u>Walking</u> — <u>1.4 m/s</u> (5 km/h)
> <u>Running</u> — <u>3 m/s</u> (11 km/h)
> <u>Cycling</u> — <u>5.5 m/s</u> (20 km/h)

> <u>Cars</u> in a <u>built-up area</u> — <u>13 m/s</u> (47 km/h)
> <u>Cars</u> on a <u>motorway</u> — <u>31 m/s</u> (112 km/h)
> <u>Aeroplanes</u> — <u>250 m/s</u> (900 km/h)
> <u>Trains</u> — up to <u>55 m/s</u> (200 km/h)
> <u>Ferries</u> — 15 m/s (54 km/h)

> <u>Wind</u> speed — <u>5 – 20 m/s</u>
> Speed of <u>sound</u> in <u>air</u> — <u>340 m/s</u>

You can use **Different Equipment** to Measure **Distance** and **Time**

To <u>calculate</u> speed you'll need measurements of <u>distance</u> and <u>time</u>. For distances less than 1 m and times greater than 5 s, you'll probably use a <u>stopwatch</u> and a <u>metre ruler</u>, but there are <u>many different ways</u> to take distance and time measurements:

1) Light gates (p.138) are often the best option for <u>short</u> time intervals. They get rid of the <u>human error</u> caused by <u>reaction times</u> (p.36).

2) For finding something like a person's <u>walking speed</u>, the distances and times you'll look at are quite <u>large</u>. You can use a <u>rolling tape measure</u> (one of those clicky wheel things) and <u>markers</u> to measure and mark out distances.

3) If you're feeling a bit high-tech, you could also record a <u>video</u> of the moving object and look at how <u>far</u> it travels each <u>frame</u>. If you know how many <u>frames per second</u> the camera records, you can find the <u>distance</u> travelled by the object in a given number of frames and the <u>time</u> that it takes to do so.

Acceleration

Acceleration is the rate of change of velocity. You need to be able estimate some day to day accelerations. This might take you a while at first, but over time you should get faster.

Acceleration is How Quickly You're Speeding Up

1) Acceleration is definitely not the same as velocity or speed.

2) Acceleration is the change in velocity in a certain amount of time.

3) You can find the average acceleration of an object using:

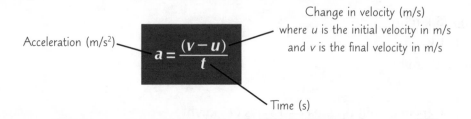

Acceleration (m/s^2)

$$a = \frac{(v - u)}{t}$$

Change in velocity (m/s)
where u is the initial velocity in m/s
and v is the final velocity in m/s

Time (s)

4) Initial velocity is just the starting velocity of the object.

5) Negative acceleration is deceleration (if something slows down, the change in velocity is negative).

You Need to be Able to Estimate Accelerations

You might have to estimate the acceleration (or deceleration) of an object:

EXAMPLE: **A car is travelling at 15 m/s, when it collides with a tree and comes to a stop. Estimate the deceleration of the car.**

1) Estimate how long it would take the car to stop.   The car comes to a stop in ~1 s.

The ~ symbol just means it's an approximate value (or answer).

2) Put these numbers into the acceleration equation. $a = (v - u) \div t$

3) As the car has slowed down,
the change in velocity and so the acceleration
is negative — the car is decelerating.

$= (0 - 15) \div 1$

$= -15 \text{ m/s}^2$

So the deceleration is about 15 m/s^2

From the deceleration, you can estimate the forces involved too — more about that on page 38.

Acceleration doesn't always have to mean getting faster or slower...

Acceleration measures how quickly velocity changes. Speeding up or slowing down is one way in which velocity can change — but not the only way. Velocity can also change in direction. So, although it might seem weird, a car driving round a roundabout at constant speed is actually experiencing acceleration.

Acceleration

For cases of <u>constant acceleration</u>, which includes pretty much anything that's falling, there's a really useful <u>equation</u> you can use to calculate all sorts of <u>variables</u> of <u>motion</u>.

Uniform Acceleration Means a Constant Acceleration

1) <u>Constant acceleration</u> is sometimes called <u>uniform acceleration</u>.

2) Acceleration <u>due to gravity</u> (g) is <u>uniform</u> for objects in free fall. It's roughly equal to <u>10 m/s^2</u> near the Earth's surface and has the same value as gravitational field strength (p.30).

3) You can use this <u>equation</u> for <u>uniform</u> acceleration:

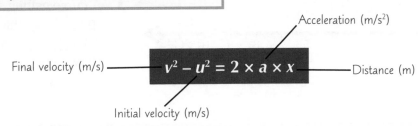

Acceleration (m/s^2)

Final velocity (m/s)

$$v^2 - u^2 = 2 \times a \times x$$

Distance (m)

Initial velocity (m/s)

EXAMPLE:

A van travelling at 23 m/s starts decelerating uniformly at 2.0 m/s^2 as it heads towards a built-up area 112 m away.

What will its speed be when it reaches the built-up area?

1) First, <u>rearrange</u> the equation so v^2 is on one side. $v^2 = u^2 + (2 \times a \times x)$

2) Now put the <u>numbers</u> in — remember a is <u>negative</u> because it's a deceleration. $v^2 = 23^2 + (2 \times -2.0 \times 112)$
$= 81$

3) Finally, <u>square root</u> the whole thing. $v = \sqrt{81} = 9$ m/s

EXAMPLE:

A ball is launched from the ground, directly upwards, at an initial speed of 14 m/s.

What is the maximum height the ball will reach? (You may ignore air resistance.)

1) This time you'll need to <u>rearrange</u> the equation so x is on one side. $x = (v^2 - u^2) \div (2 \times a)$

2) Again, put the <u>numbers</u> in — this is a little trickier. Remember a is negative as the ball is decelerating. Also the final velocity, at the instant the ball peaks, will be 0 m/s. $x = (0^2 - 14^2) \div (2 \times (-10))$
$x = (-196) \div (-20)$
$x = 9.8$ m

Acceleration due to gravity is 10 m/s^2 in an ideal world...

You might be thinking 'acceleration due to gravity can't have the same value, g, for <u>all objects</u> — I know a bowling ball falls faster than a feather'. This is because <u>air resistance</u> has a much bigger <u>effect</u> on the feather's <u>motion</u>. If <u>gravity</u> were the <u>only force</u> acting, they really would <u>accelerate</u> at the <u>same rate</u>.

Distance/Time Graphs

It's time for some exciting graphs. Distance/time graphs contain a lot of information, but they can look a bit complicated. Read on to get to grips with the rules of the graphs, and all will become clear.

Distance/Time Graphs Tell You How Far Something has Travelled

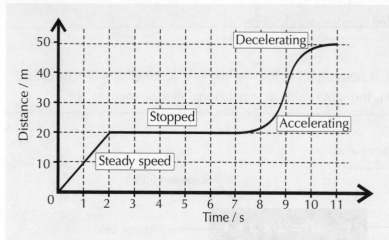

The different parts of a distance/time graph describe the motion of an object:

- The gradient (slope) at any point gives the speed of the object.
- Flat sections are where it's stopped.
- A steeper graph means it's going faster.
- Curves represent acceleration.
- A curve getting steeper means it's speeding up (increasing gradient).
- A levelling off curve means it's slowing down (decreasing gradient).

The Speed of an Object can be Found From a Distance/Time Graph

You can find the speed at any time on a distance/time graph:

1) If the graph is a straight line, the speed at any point along that line is equal to the gradient of the line.

> For example, in the graph above, the speed at any time between 0 s and 2 s is:
>
> $$\text{Speed} = \text{gradient} = \frac{\text{change in the vertical}}{\text{change in the horizontal}} = \frac{20}{2} = \underline{10 \text{ m/s}}$$

2) If the graph is curved, to find the speed at a certain time you need to draw a tangent to the curve at that point, and then find the gradient of the tangent.

A tangent is a line that is parallel to the curve at that point.

3) You can also calculate the average speed of an object when it has non-uniform motion (i.e. it's accelerating) by dividing the total distance travelled by the time it takes to travel that distance.

EXAMPLE:

The graph shows the distance/time graph for a cyclist on his bike.
Calculate:
a) the speed of the bike 25 s into the journey.
b) the average speed of the cyclist from 0 to 30 s.

1) Draw the tangent to the curve at 25 s (red line).

2) Then calculate the gradient of the tangent (blue lines).

$$\text{gradient} = \frac{\text{change in the vertical}}{\text{change in the horizontal}} = \frac{80}{10} = 8 \text{ m/s}$$

So, the speed of the bike 25 s into the journey is 8 m/s.

3) Use the formula from page 19 to find the average speed of the bike.

average speed = distance ÷ time = 150 ÷ 30 = 5 m/s

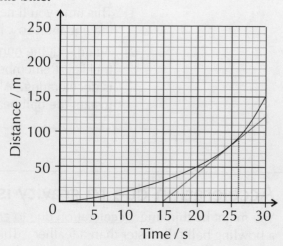

Velocity/Time Graphs

Even more graphs — <u>velocity/time graphs</u> this time. These look a lot like the <u>distance/time graphs</u> on page 22, so make sure you check the labels on the axes really carefully. You don't want to mix them up.

Velocity/Time Graphs can have a Positive or Negative Gradient

How an object's <u>velocity</u> changes over time can be plotted on a <u>velocity/time</u> (or *v/t*) graph.

1) <u>Gradient = acceleration</u>,
   since acceleration = change in velocity ÷ time.

2) <u>Flat sections</u> represent a <u>steady speed</u>.

3) The <u>steeper</u> the graph, the <u>greater</u> the
   <u>acceleration</u> or <u>deceleration</u>.

4) <u>Uphill</u> sections (/) are <u>acceleration</u>.

5) <u>Downhill</u> sections (\) are <u>deceleration</u>.

6) A <u>curve</u> means <u>changing acceleration</u>.

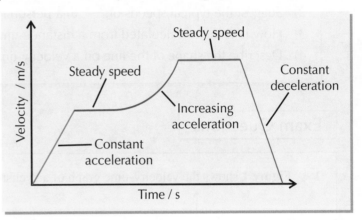

If the graph is curved, you can use a tangent to the curve (p.22) at a point to find the acceleration at that point.

The Distance Travelled is the Area Under the Graph

1) The <u>area</u> under any section of the graph (or all of it)
   is equal to the <u>distance travelled</u> in that <u>time interval</u>.

2) For bits of the graph where the acceleration's <u>constant</u>,
   you can split the area into <u>rectangles</u> and <u>triangles</u> to work it out.

3) You can also find the <u>area</u> under the graph
   by <u>counting the squares</u> under the line and <u>multiplying</u>
   the number by the value of <u>one square</u>.

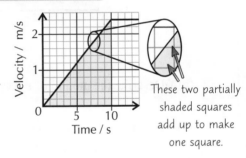

These two partially shaded squares add up to make one square.

EXAMPLE:

The velocity/time graph of a car's journey is plotted.

a)   Calculate the acceleration of the car over the first 10 s.

b)   How far does the car travel in the first 15 s of the journey?

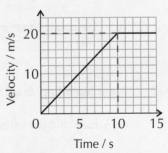

a)   This is just the <u>gradient</u> of the line: $a = (v - u) \div t$
                                                        $= (20 - 0) \div 10 = 2 \text{ m/s}^2$

b)   <u>Split</u> the area into a <u>triangle</u> and   OR   b)   Find the <u>value</u> of <u>one square</u>,
     a <u>rectangle</u>, then <u>add</u> together their   <u>count</u> the <u>total</u> number of squares
     areas — remember the area of a   under the line, and then <u>multiply</u>
     triangle is ½ × base × height.   these two values together.

     Area = (½ × 10 × 20) + (5 × 20)   1 square = 2 m/s × 1 s = 2 m
          = 200 m   Area = 100 squares
                                                                       = 100 × 2 = 200 m

Warm-Up & Exam Questions

Slow down, it's not time to move on to the next topic just yet. First it's time to check that all the stuff you've just read is still running around your brain. Dive into these questions.

Warm-Up Questions

1) What is the difference between speed and velocity?
2) Suggest the typical speeds of: a) a person running,   b) an aeroplane,   c) sound in air.
3) How is velocity calculated from a distance-time graph?
4) Describe the shape of the line on a velocity-time graph for an object travelling at a steady speed.

Exam Questions

1 **Figure 1** shows the velocity-time graph of a cyclist.

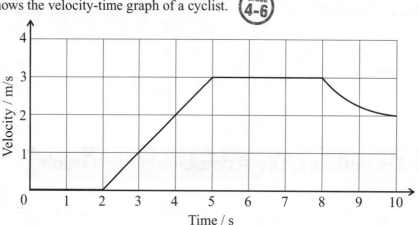

Figure 1

(a)   Describe the motion of the cyclist between 5 and 10 seconds.

[2 marks]

(b)   Calculate how far the cyclist travelled between 2 and 5 seconds.

[2 marks]

(c)   Calculate the acceleration of the cyclist between 2 and 5 seconds.

[2 marks]

(d)   Calculate the average deceleration of the cyclist between 8 and 10 seconds.

[3 marks]

2   A car travelling down the motorway has to perform an emergency stop. Grade 6-7

(a)   Estimate the original speed of the car in metres per second.

[1 mark]

(b)   After pressing the brake pedal, the car decelerates uniformly for 5 seconds until reaching a complete stop.

(i) Calculate the deceleration the car experiences.

[2 marks]

(ii) Calculate the distance travelled by the car in this time.
     Use the correct equation from the Physics Equation Sheet on the inside back cover.

[3 marks]

Newton's First and Second Laws

Way back in the 1660s, some clever chap named <u>Isaac Newton</u> worked out some <u>Laws of Motion</u>...

A **Force** is Needed to **Change Motion**

This may seem simple, but it's important. <u>Newton's First Law</u> says that a resultant force (p.89) is needed to make something <u>start moving</u>, <u>speed up</u> or <u>slow down</u>:

> If the resultant force on a <u>stationary</u> object is <u>zero</u>, the object will <u>remain stationary</u>. If the <u>resultant force</u> on a moving object is <u>zero</u>, it'll just carry on moving at the <u>same velocity</u> (same speed <u>and</u> direction).

stationary bus

So, when a train or car or bus or anything else is <u>moving</u> at a <u>constant velocity</u>, the resistive and driving <u>forces</u> on it must all be <u>balanced</u>. The velocity will only change if there's a <u>non-zero</u> resultant force acting on the object.

bus with constant velocity

1) A non-zero <u>resultant</u> force will always produce <u>acceleration</u> (or deceleration) in the <u>direction of the force</u>.

2) This "<u>acceleration</u>" can take <u>five</u> different forms: <u>starting</u>, <u>stopping</u>, <u>speeding up</u>, <u>slowing down</u> and <u>changing direction</u>.

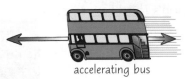

accelerating bus

Newton's First Law Helps to Describe **Circular Motion**

1) Velocity is both the <u>speed</u> and <u>direction</u> of an object (p.18).

2) If an object is travelling in a <u>circular orbit</u> (at a <u>constant speed</u>) it is <u>constantly changing direction</u>, so it is constantly <u>changing velocity</u>. This means it's <u>accelerating</u>.

3) From Newton's First Law, this means there <u>must</u> be a <u>resultant force</u> (p.89) acting on it.

4) This force acts towards the <u>centre</u> of the circle.

5) This force that keeps something moving in a circle is called a <u>centripetal force</u>.

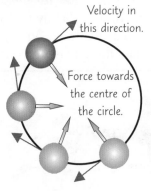

Velocity in this direction.

Force towards the centre of the circle.

Acceleration is **Proportional** to the **Resultant Force**

1) The <u>larger</u> the <u>resultant force</u> acting on an object, the <u>more</u> the object accelerates — the force and the acceleration are <u>directly proportional</u>. You can write this as $F \propto a$.

2) Acceleration is also <u>inversely proportional</u> to the <u>mass</u> of the object — so an object with a <u>larger</u> mass will accelerate <u>less</u> than one with a smaller mass (for a <u>fixed resultant force</u>).

3) There's an incredibly <u>useful formula</u> that describes <u>Newton's Second Law</u>:

Resultant force (N) —— $F = m \times a$ —— Acceleration (m/s^2)

Mass (kg)

EXAMPLE:

A van of mass of 2080 kg has an engine that provides a driving force of 5200 N. At 70 mph the drag force acting on the van is 5148 N. Find its acceleration at 70 mph.

1) Work out the <u>resultant force</u> on the van. (Drawing a <u>free body diagram</u> may help.)

Resultant force = 5200 − 5148 = 52 N

2) <u>Rearrange</u> $F = m \times a$ and stick in the <u>values</u> you know.

$a = F \div m$
$= 52 \div 2080 = 0.025$ m/s^2

Inertia and Newton's Third Law

Newton's Third Law and inertia sound pretty straightforward, but things can quickly get confusing...

Inertia is the Tendency for Motion to Remain Unchanged

1) Until acted on by a resultant force, objects at rest stay at rest and objects moving at a constant velocity will stay moving at that velocity (Newton's First Law).

2) This tendency to keep moving with the same velocity is called inertia.

3) An object's inertial mass measures how difficult it is to change the velocity of an object.

4) Inertial mass can be found using Newton's Second Law of $F = m \times a$ (p.25). Rearranging this gives $m = F \div a$, so inertial mass is just the ratio of force over acceleration.

Newton's Third Law — Interaction Pairs are Equal and Opposite

Newton's Third Law says:

> When two objects interact, the forces they exert on each other are equal and opposite.

1) If you push something, say a shopping trolley, the trolley will push back against you, just as hard.

2) And as soon as you stop pushing, so does the trolley. Kinda clever really.

3) So far so good. The slightly tricky thing to get your head round is this — if the forces are always equal, how does anything ever go anywhere? The important thing to remember is that the two forces are acting on different objects.

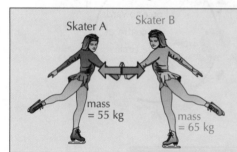
Skater A   Skater B
mass = 55 kg   mass = 65 kg

When skater A pushes on skater B, she feels an equal and opposite force from skater B's hand (the 'normal contact' force). Both skaters feel the same sized force, in opposite directions, and so accelerate away from each other.

Skater A will be accelerated more than skater B, though, because she has a smaller mass — remember $a = F \div m$.

An example of Newton's Third Law in an equilibrium situation is a man pushing against a wall. As the man pushes the wall, there is a normal contact force acting back on him. These two forces are the same size. As the man applies a force and pushes the wall, the wall 'pushes back' on him with an equal force.

Push   Normal contact force

It can be easy to get confused with Newton's Third Law when an object is in equilibrium. E.g. a book resting on a table is in equilibrium. The weight of the book is equal to the normal contact force. The weight of the book pulls it down, and the normal contact force from the table pushes it up. This is NOT Newton's Third Law. These forces are different types and they're both acting on the book.

The pairs of forces due to Newton's Third Law in this case are:

1) The weight of book is pulled down by gravity from Earth (W_B) and the book also pulls back up on the Earth (W_E).

2) The normal contact force from the table pushing up on the book (N_B) and the normal contact force from the book pushing down on the table (N_T).

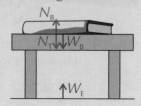
N_B
N_T W_B
W_E

Warm-Up & Exam Questions

Now you've gotten yourself on the right side of the law(s of motion), it's time to put your knowledge on trial. Have a go at cross-examining these questions.

Warm-Up Questions

1) What is the resultant force on an object moving at a constant velocity?
2) Write down the formula that links mass, force and acceleration.
3) True or false? An object travelling at a constant speed around a circular path is not accelerating.
4) Boulders A and B are accelerated from 0 m/s to 5 m/s in 10 s. Boulder A required a force of 70 N, and Boulder B required a force of 95 N. Which boulder has the greater inertial mass?
5) True or false? Two interacting objects exert equal and opposite forces on each other.

Exam Questions

1   A student has a cricket bat with a mass of 1.2 kg.
She uses it to hit a ball with a mass of 160 g forwards with a force of 500 N.

   (a)   State the force that the ball exerts on the bat. Explain your answer.

[2 marks]

   (b)   State and explain whether the acceleration of the ball is greater or smaller than the acceleration of the bat.

[2 marks]

2   A camper van has a mass of 2500 kg. It is driven along a straight, level road at a constant speed of 90.0 kilometres per hour, as shown in **Figure 1**.

Figure 1

   (a)   A headwind begins to blow, so that the resultant force acting on the van is 200 N in the opposite direction to the van's motion. This causes the van to slow down. Calculate the van's deceleration.

[3 marks]

The van begins travelling at a constant speed before colliding with a stationary 4.50 kg traffic cone. The traffic cone accelerates in the direction of the van's motion with an acceleration of 28.0 m/s^2.

   (b)   Calculate the force applied to the traffic cone by the van.

[2 marks]

   (c)   Calculate the deceleration of the van, due to the force of the cone, during the collision.

[3 marks]

Investigating Motion

Here comes a <u>Core Practical</u>. This one's all about testing <u>Newton's Second Law</u>. It uses some nifty bits of kit that you may not have seen before, so make sure you follow the instructions closely.

You can **Investigate** the Motion of a **Trolley** on a **Ramp**

It's time for an experiment that tests <u>Newton's 2nd Law</u>, $F = m \times a$ (p.25).

1) Measure the <u>mass</u> of the <u>trolley</u>, the <u>unit masses</u> and the <u>hanging hook</u>.
   Measure the <u>length</u> of the piece of <u>card</u> which will <u>interrupt</u> the light gate beams.
   Then set up your <u>apparatus</u> as shown in the diagram below, but <u>don't</u> attach the string to the trolley.

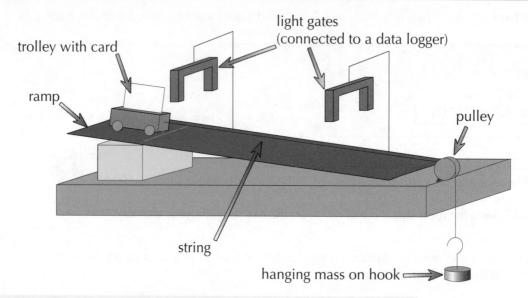

light gates
(connected to a data logger)

trolley with card

ramp

pulley

string

hanging mass on hook ➜

2) <u>Adjust</u> the <u>height</u> of the ramp until the trolley <u>just</u> starts to move.
   This means that the <u>force due to gravity</u> acting on the <u>hanging mass</u> will
   be the <u>main</u> cause of the trolley <u>accelerating</u> as it travels down the ramp.

3) Mark a <u>line</u> on the ramp just before the first <u>light gate</u>, so the trolley travels the <u>same distance</u>
   every time. The light gate will record the <u>initial speed</u> of the trolley as it <u>begins to move</u>.

4) <u>Attach the trolley</u> to the hanging mass by the string. Hold the trolley <u>still</u>
   at the start line, and then <u>let go</u> of it so that it starts to roll down the slope.

5) The <u>weight</u> of the <u>hook</u> and any <u>masses</u> attached to it will provide the <u>accelerating force</u>,
   equal to the <u>mass of the hook</u> (m) × <u>acceleration due to gravity</u> (g).
   The <u>weight</u> of the hook and masses accelerates <u>both</u> the trolley and the masses, so you
   are investigating the acceleration of the <u>system</u> (the trolley <u>and</u> the masses together).

6) Each <u>light gate</u> will record the <u>time</u> when the trolley passes through it and the <u>speed</u>
   of the trolley at that time. The <u>acceleration</u> of the trolley can then be found using
   <u>acceleration = change in speed ÷ time</u>, with the following values:

   • the <u>initial speed</u> of the trolley as it passes through the <u>first light gate</u> (it'll be <u>roughly</u> 0 m/s),

   • the <u>final speed</u> of the trolley, as it passes through the <u>second light gate</u>,

   • the <u>time</u> it takes the trolley to travel <u>between</u> the two light gates.

7) <u>Repeat</u> the experiment at least <u>three times</u> and calculate an <u>average acceleration</u> from the results.

Investigating Motion

Now you've set up the <u>equipment</u>, and you're used to how it works, it's time to start <u>adjusting</u> your <u>variables</u>. Take care with the <u>method</u> here — there are some important points you don't want to miss.

Varying Mass and Force

1) To investigate how the <u>mass</u> of the system affects its <u>acceleration</u>, <u>add masses</u> one at a time to the <u>trolley</u>.

2) <u>Don't add masses to the hook</u>, as this will change the force acting on the system.

3) Each time you add a mass to the trolley, take a <u>measurement</u> of the system's <u>average acceleration</u> using the <u>method</u> described in points 2-7 on the <u>previous page</u>.

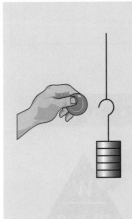

1) To investigate how the <u>force</u> acting on the system affects its <u>acceleration</u>, you need to keep the <u>total mass</u> of the <u>system</u> the <u>same</u>, but <u>change</u> the mass on the <u>hook</u>.

2) To do this, start with <u>all</u> the masses loaded onto the <u>trolley</u>, and <u>transfer</u> the masses to the hook one at a time, to increase the <u>accelerating force</u> (the weight of the hanging masses).

3) The mass of the system stays the same as you're only <u>transferring</u> the masses from <u>one part</u> of the system (the trolley) to another (the hook).

4) Each time you transfer a mass from the trolley to the hook, take a <u>measurement</u> of the system's <u>average acceleration</u> using the <u>method</u> described in points 2-7 on the <u>previous page</u>.

Newton's Second Law Can Explain the Results

1) <u>Newton's Second Law</u> can be written as $F = m \times a$. Here, F = <u>weight</u> of the <u>hanging masses</u>, m = mass of the <u>whole system</u> and a = <u>acceleration</u> of the <u>system</u>.

2) By <u>adding</u> masses to the <u>trolley</u>, the mass of the <u>whole system</u> increases, but the <u>force</u> applied to the system stays the <u>same</u>. This should lead to a decrease in the <u>acceleration of the trolley</u>, so a is inversely proportional to m ($a = F \div m$).

3) By <u>transferring masses</u> to the hook, you are <u>increasing the accelerating force</u> without changing the <u>mass</u> of the whole system. <u>Increasing</u> the force should lead to an <u>increase</u> in the acceleration of the trolley, so a is proportional to F.

This experiment has a lot of steps, so don't speed through it...

Make sure the <u>string</u> is the <u>right length</u> and there's <u>enough space</u> for the hanging masses to <u>fall</u>. There needs to be enough space so that the masses <u>don't</u> hit the floor <u>before</u> the trolley has <u>passed through the light gate fully</u> — if they hit the floor, the force won't be applied the whole way through the trolley's journey, so you won't get an accurate measurement for the <u>speed</u>.

Weight

Now for something a bit more <u>attractive</u> — the force of <u>gravity</u>. Enjoy...

Weight and Mass are Not the Same

1) <u>Mass</u> is just the <u>amount of 'stuff'</u> in an object. For any given object this will have the same value <u>anywhere</u> in the universe.

2) Mass is a <u>scalar</u> quantity. It's measured in <u>kilograms</u> with a <u>mass</u> balance (an old-fashioned pair of balancing scales).

Gravity attracts all masses, but you only notice it when one of the masses is really big (like a planet).

3) <u>Weight</u> is the <u>force</u> acting on an object due to <u>gravity</u> (the <u>pull</u> of the <u>gravitational force</u> on the object). Close to Earth, this <u>force</u> is caused by the <u>gravitational field</u> around the Earth.

4) Weight is a <u>force</u> measured in <u>newtons</u>. You can think of the force as acting from a <u>single point</u> on the object, called its <u>centre of mass</u> (a point at which you assume the <u>whole</u> mass is concentrated).

5) Weight is measured using a calibrated <u>spring</u> balance (or <u>newton meter</u>).

Weight Depends on Mass and Gravitational Field Strength

1) You can calculate the <u>weight</u> of an object if you know its <u>mass</u> (m) and the <u>strength</u> of the <u>gravitational field</u> that it is in (g):

weight (N) = mass (kg) × gravitational field strength (N/kg)

2) Gravitational field <u>strength</u> varies with <u>location</u>. It's <u>stronger</u> the <u>closer</u> you are to the mass causing the field (and <u>more massive</u> objects create <u>stronger</u> fields).

3) This means that the weight of an object <u>changes</u> with its location.

EXAMPLE:

What is the weight, in newtons, of a 2.0 kg object on Earth (g = 10 N/kg)?

1) Calculate the weight on <u>Earth</u> using the equation for <u>weight</u> given above.

$W = m \times g = 2.0 \times 10 = 20$ N

The object has a weight of 16 N on a different planet. What is the gravitational field strength of this other planet?

1) <u>Rearrange</u> the weight equation for g.
2) <u>Substitute</u> the values in.

$g = W \div m$
$= 16 \div 2.0 = 8.0$ N/kg

Remember — the mass of the object is the same on every planet, it's the weight of the object that changes.

You might be experiencing déjà vu...

On p.21 you saw that 'g' was introduced as '<u>acceleration due to gravity</u>' (m/s²), and now it's being used for '<u>gravitational field strength</u>' (N/kg). These two quantities <u>have been given the same symbol</u> because acceleration due to a gravitational field will always be <u>equal</u> to the strength of that field.

Warm-Up & Exam Questions

That's all you need to know about gravitational field strength... I bet that's a weight off your mind.
Try out these questions and see how much really sunk in.

Warm-Up Questions

1) When carrying out the trolley-and-ramp practical (p.28), what is the purpose of adjusting the ramp so that the trolley is just about to move?

2) Give the definitions of mass and weight.

3) What are the units of weight?

Exam Questions

1 On Earth, the gravitational field strength is 10 N/kg.
Calculate the weight of an 80 kg person on Earth.

[2 marks]

PRACTICAL

2 A student investigates how the mass of a system
affects its acceleration.
Figure 1 is a graph of her results.

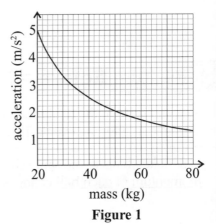

(a) Name the independent variable in this experiment.

[1 mark]

(b) Name the dependent variable in this experiment.

[1 mark]

(c) Describe the relationship between mass and acceleration.

[1 mark]

Figure 1

3 The weight of a space probe on the surface of Mars
is 0.4 times its weight on the surface of Earth.

(a) The gravitational field strength on Earth is 10 N/kg.
Determine the gravitational field strength of Mars.

[2 marks]

(b) The weight of the probe on Mars is 3600 N. Calculate the mass of the probe.

[3 marks]

PRACTICAL

4* A student is investigating how acceleration varies with force.
He has a 1 kg trolley, attached by a pulley to a 0.5 kg hanging hook.
He also has eight 100 g masses. When the trolley is released, it rolls down a ramp,
and passes through two sets of light gates which each measure its velocity.

Describe an experiment that the student can perform using this equipment
to investigate the relationship between force and acceleration.

[6 marks]

Momentum

A <u>large rugby player</u> running very <u>fast</u> has much <u>more momentum</u> than a <u>skinny</u> bloke out for a Sunday afternoon <u>stroll</u>. Momentum's something that <u>all moving objects have</u>, so you better get your head around it.

Momentum = Mass × Velocity

Momentum is mainly about how much 'oomph' an object has. It's a <u>property</u> that <u>all moving objects have</u>.

1) The <u>greater</u> the <u>mass</u> of an object, or the <u>greater</u> its <u>velocity</u>, the <u>more momentum</u> the object has.
2) Momentum is a <u>vector</u> quantity — it has size <u>and</u> direction.
3) You can <u>work out</u> the momentum of an object using:

$$p = m \times v$$

momentum (kg m/s) = mass (kg) × velocity (m/s)

EXAMPLE:

A 50 kg cheetah is running at 60 m/s. Calculate its momentum.

$p = m \times v = 50 \times 60 = 3000$ kg m/s

EXAMPLE:

A boy has a mass of 30 kg and a momentum of 75 kg m/s. Calculate his velocity.

$v = p \div m = 75 \div 30 = 2.5$ m/s

Momentum Before = Momentum After

In a <u>closed system</u>, the total momentum <u>before</u> an event (e.g. a collision) is the same as <u>after</u> the event. This is called <u>conservation of momentum</u>.

A closed system is just a fancy way of saying that no external forces act.

In snooker, balls of the <u>same size</u> and <u>mass</u> collide with each other. Each collision is an <u>event</u> where the <u>momentum</u> of <u>each ball changes</u>, but the <u>overall</u> momentum <u>stays the same</u> (momentum is <u>conserved</u>).

Before: The red ball is <u>stationary</u>, so it has <u>zero momentum</u>. The white ball is moving with a velocity v, so has <u>momentum</u> of $p = m \times v$.

After: The white ball hits the red ball, causing it to <u>move</u>. The red ball now has <u>momentum</u>. The white ball <u>continues</u> moving, but at a much <u>smaller velocity</u> (and so a much <u>smaller momentum</u>). The <u>combined</u> momentum of the red and white ball is equal to the <u>original</u> momentum of the white ball, $m \times v$.

A <u>moving car</u> hits into the back of a <u>parked car</u>. The crash causes the two cars to <u>lock together</u>, and they <u>continue moving</u> in the direction that the original moving car was travelling, but at a <u>lower velocity</u>.

Before: The momentum was equal to mass of moving car × its velocity.
After: The <u>mass</u> of the moving object has <u>increased</u>, but its momentum is equal to the momentum <u>before the collision</u>. So an <u>increase</u> in <u>mass</u> causes a <u>decrease</u> in <u>velocity</u>.

If the momentum <u>before</u> an event is <u>zero</u>, then the momentum <u>after</u> will also be <u>zero</u>. E.g. in an <u>explosion</u>, the momentum before is zero. After the explosion, the pieces fly off in <u>different directions</u>, so that the total momentum <u>cancels out</u> to zero.

Momentum

You can use the <u>equation</u> for <u>momentum</u>, along with the <u>conservation of momentum principle</u>, to <u>calculate</u> changes in <u>mass</u> and <u>velocity</u> in interactions. It's all about '<u>momentum before = momentum after</u>'.

Calculations using Conservation of Momentum

You've already seen that <u>momentum is conserved</u> in a <u>closed system</u> (see last page).
You can use this to help you calculate things like the <u>velocity</u> or <u>mass</u> of objects in an event (e.g. a collision).

EXAMPLE:

Misha fires a paintball gun. A 3.0 g paintball is fired at a velocity of 90 m/s. Calculate the velocity at which the paintball gun recoils if it has a mass of 1.5 kg. Momentum is conserved.

The word recoil means to move backwards.

1) Calculate the <u>momentum</u> of the <u>pellet</u>.

$p = 0.003 \times 90 = 0.27$ kg m/s

2) The momentum before the gun is fired is <u>zero</u>. This is equal to the <u>total</u> momentum after the collision.

Momentum before = momentum after

$0 = 0.27 + (1.5 \times v)$

3) The momentum of the <u>gun</u> is $1.5 \times v$.

4) <u>Rearrange</u> the equation to find the <u>velocity</u> of the gun. The <u>minus sign</u> shows the gun is travelling in the <u>opposite direction</u> to the bullet.

$v = -(0.27 \div 1.5)$
$= -0.18$ m/s

EXAMPLE:

Two skaters, Skater A and Skater B, approach each other, collide and move off together as shown in the image on the right. At what velocity do they move after the collision?

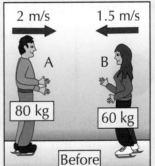

1) Choose which direction is <u>positive</u>. I'll say "<u>positive</u>" means "<u>to the right</u>".

2) <u>Total momentum before</u> collision = momentum of A + momentum of B.

Momentum before = $(80 \times 2) + (60 \times (-1.5))$
$= 70$ kg m/s

3) <u>Total momentum after</u> collision = momentum of A and B together.

Momentum after = $140 \times v$

4) Set momentum before <u>equal to</u> momentum after, and <u>rearrange</u> for the answer.

$140 \times v = 70$, so $v = 70 \div 140$
$v = 0.5$ m/s to the right

 Momentum questions may need you to analyse a scenario...

EXAM TIP

Make sure you <u>read</u> any momentum questions <u>carefully</u>. You need to identify what the <u>objects</u> and <u>momentum</u> were <u>before the interaction</u>, and what they are <u>after the interaction</u>. The question may not be a scenario you're familiar with, so you'll need to work out what's going on.

Momentum

When a resultant force acts on an object, it causes the object to change momentum.

Forces Cause Changes in Momentum

1) When a resultant force acts on an object for a certain amount of time, it causes a change in momentum. Newton's 2nd Law can explain this:

   - A resultant force on an object causes it to accelerate: force = mass × acceleration (see p.25).
   - Acceleration is just change in velocity over time, so: force = $\dfrac{\text{mass} \times \text{change in velocity}}{\text{time}}$.
     This means a force applied to an object over any time interval will change the object's velocity.
   - Mass × change in velocity is equal to change in momentum, so you end up with the equation:

   force (N) — $$F = \frac{(mv - mu)}{t}$$ — change in momentum (kg m/s)

   time (s)

2) The faster a given change in momentum happens, the bigger the force causing the change must be (i.e. if t gets smaller in the equation above, F gets bigger).

3) So if someone's momentum changes very quickly, like in a car crash, the forces on the body will be very large, and more likely to cause injury. There's more about this on p.38.

Conservation of Momentum Shows Newton's Third Law

The equation above can help to show Newton's Third Law (reaction forces are equal and opposite). Take this example using snooker balls below:

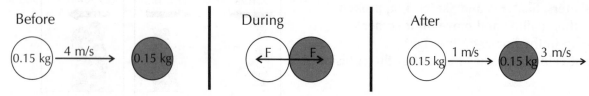

Before   During   After

1) Before the collision, the white ball has a momentum of 0.15 × 4 = 0.6 kg m/s.
2) The red ball has a momentum of zero. The total momentum of the system is 0.6 kg m/s.
3) When the balls collide, the white ball exerts a force on the red ball.
4) Due to Newton's 3rd Law, the red ball also exerts an equal but opposite force on the white ball.
5) After the collision, the white ball continues moving at 1 m/s. The red ball begins moving at 3 m/s.
6) The total momentum is (0.15 × 1) + (0.15 × 3) = 0.6 kg m/s. Momentum is conserved.
7) The collision lasted 0.1 s. Given this information, you can calculate the size of the force that caused this change of velocity (and so change of momentum) for each ball:

Red Ball	White Ball
$F = \dfrac{(mv - mu)}{t}$	$F = \dfrac{(mv - mu)}{t}$
$= \dfrac{(0.15 \times 3) - (0.15 \times 0)}{0.1}$	$= \dfrac{(0.15 \times 1) - (0.15 \times 4)}{0.1}$
$= \dfrac{0.45}{0.1} = 4.5 \text{ N}$	$= \dfrac{-0.45}{0.1} = -4.5 \text{ N}$

8) The force exerted on the white ball (by the red ball) is equal and opposite to the force exerted on the red ball (by the white ball). This shows Newton's Third Law.

Warm-Up & Exam Questions

Don't lose momentum now. Throw yourself into these questions and you'll be done before you know it.

Warm-Up Questions

1) What are the units of momentum?
2) What is meant by the conservation of momentum?
3) What is the total momentum before and after an explosion?
4) How does increasing the time over which an object changes momentum change the force on it?

Exam Questions

1   A 60 kg gymnast lands on a crash mat. When they hit the crash mat, they are moving at 5.0 m/s and come to a stop in a period of 1.2 seconds (after which their momentum is zero).

   (a)   State the equation linking momentum, mass and velocity.

[1 mark]

   (b)   Calculate the momentum of the gymnast immediately before they hit the crash mat.

[2 marks]

   (c)   Calculate the size of the average force acting on the gymnast as they land on the crash mat. Use the correct equation from the Physics Equation Sheet on the inside back cover.

[2 marks]

2   In a demolition derby, cars drive around an arena and crash into each other.

   (a)   One car has a mass of 650 kg and a velocity of 15.0 m/s. Calculate the momentum of the car.

[2 marks]

   (b)   The car collides head-on with another car with a mass of 750 kg. The two cars stick together. Calculate the combined velocity of the two cars immediately after the collision if the other car had a velocity of −10.0 m/s before the collision. Give your answer to 3 significant figures.

[4 marks]

3   A fast-moving neutron collides with a uranium-235 atom and bounces off. **Figure 1** shows the particles before and after the collision. The masses given in **Figure 1** are relative masses.

BEFORE	**AFTER**

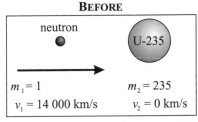 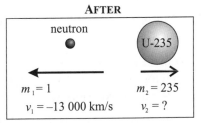

Figure 1

Calculate the velocity of the U-235 atom after the collision. Give your answer to 3 significant figures.

[4 marks]

Reaction Times

Believe it or not, <u>reaction times</u> measure how quickly you react. They're also super easy to <u>test</u> for yourself. Read on for a simple <u>experiment</u> you can do in the lab.

You can **Measure** Reaction Times with the **Ruler Drop Test**

Everyone's <u>reaction time</u> is different and many different factors can affect it.

You can do <u>simple experiments</u> to investigate your reaction time, but as reaction times are <u>so short</u>, you haven't got a chance of measuring one with a <u>stopwatch</u>. One way of measuring reaction times is to use a <u>computer-based test</u> (e.g. <u>clicking a mouse</u> when the screen changes colour). Another is the <u>ruler drop test</u>.

Here's how to carry it out:

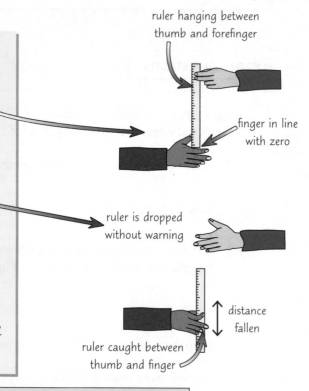

ruler hanging between thumb and forefinger

finger in line with zero

ruler is dropped without warning

distance fallen

ruler caught between thumb and finger

1) Sit with your arm resting on the edge of a table (this should stop you moving your arm up or down during the test). Get someone else to hold a ruler so it <u>hangs between</u> your thumb and forefinger, lined up with <u>zero</u>. You may need a <u>third person</u> to be at <u>eye level with the ruler</u> to check it's lined up.

2) Without giving any warning, the person holding the ruler should <u>drop it</u>. Close your thumb and finger to try to <u>catch the ruler as quickly as possible</u>.

3) The measurement on the ruler at the point where it is caught is <u>how far</u> the ruler dropped in the time it takes you to react.

4) The <u>longer</u> the <u>distance</u>, the <u>longer</u> the <u>reaction time</u>.

5) You can calculate <u>how long</u> the ruler falls for (the <u>reaction</u> time) because <u>acceleration due to gravity is constant</u> (roughly 10 m/s²).

E.g. say you catch the ruler at 20 cm. From p.21 you know: $\underline{v^2 - u^2 = 2 \times a \times x}$.
$u = 0$, $a = 10$ m/s² and $x = 0.2$ m, so: $v = \sqrt{2 \times 10 \times 0.2 + 0}$ = <u>2 m/s</u>
v is equal to the <u>change in velocity</u> of the ruler.
From page 20 you also know: $\underline{a = (v - u) \div t}$ so $\underline{t = (v - u) \div a = 2 \div 10 = 0.2}$ s
This gives your <u>reaction time</u>.

6) It's <u>pretty hard</u> to do this experiment <u>accurately</u>, so you should do a lot of <u>repeats</u> and calculate a <u>mean reaction time</u>. The results will be better if the ruler falls <u>straight down</u> — you could add a <u>blob of modelling clay</u> to the bottom to stop it from waving about.

7) Make sure it's a <u>fair test</u> — use the <u>same ruler</u> for each repeat, and have the <u>same person</u> dropping it.

8) You could try to investigate some factors affecting reaction time, e.g. you could introduce <u>distractions</u> by having some <u>music</u> playing or by having someone <u>talk to you</u> while the test takes place (see the next page for more on the factors affecting reaction time).

9) Remember to still do lots of <u>repeats</u> and calculate the <u>mean</u> reaction time with distractions, which you can <u>compare</u> to the mean reaction time <u>without</u> distractions.

For an experiment like this, a typical reaction time is around <u>0.2-0.6 s</u>.
A person's reaction time in a <u>real</u> situation (e.g. when driving) will be <u>longer</u> than that, though.
Typically, an <u>alert</u> driver will have a reaction time of about <u>1 s</u>.

Stopping Distances

Knowing what affects <u>stopping distances</u> is especially useful for everyday life, as well as the exam.

Stopping Distance = Thinking Distance + Braking Distance

In an <u>emergency</u>, a driver may perform an <u>emergency stop</u>. This is where the <u>maximum force</u> is applied by the <u>brakes</u> in order to stop the car in the <u>shortest possible distance</u>. The <u>longer</u> it takes a car to <u>stop</u> after seeing a hazard, the <u>higher</u> the risk of <u>crashing</u>.

The distance it takes to stop a car (<u>stopping distance</u>) is found by:

Stopping Distance = Thinking Distance + Braking Distance

<u>Thinking distance</u> is the distance the car travels in the driver's <u>reaction time</u> (the time between <u>noticing the hazard</u> and <u>applying the brakes</u>).

<u>Braking distance</u> is the distance taken to stop <u>once the brakes have been applied</u>.

Many Factors Affect Your Total Stopping Distance

<u>Thinking distance</u> is affected by:

- Your <u>speed</u> — the <u>faster</u> you're going the <u>further</u> you'll travel during the <u>time</u> you take to <u>react</u>.
- Your <u>reaction time</u> — the longer your reaction time (see next page), the longer your <u>thinking distance</u>. This can be affected by <u>tiredness</u>, <u>drugs</u> or <u>alcohol</u>. <u>Distractions</u> can affect your <u>ability</u> to <u>react</u>.

<u>Braking distance</u> is affected by:

- Your <u>speed</u> — for a <u>given</u> braking force, the <u>faster</u> a vehicle travels, the <u>longer</u> it takes to stop.
- How much <u>friction</u> is between your <u>tyres</u> and the <u>road</u> — you're more likely to <u>skid</u> if the road is <u>dirty</u>, if it's <u>icy or wet</u> or if the tyres are <u>bald</u> (tyres must have a minimum <u>tread depth</u> of <u>1.6 mm</u>).
- How good your <u>brakes</u> are — if brakes are <u>worn</u> or <u>faulty</u>, they won't be able to apply as much <u>force</u> as well-maintained brakes, which could be dangerous when you need to brake hard.
- The <u>mass</u> of the car — a car full of <u>people</u> and <u>luggage</u> won't stop as quickly as an empty car.

In the exam, you may need to <u>spot</u> the <u>factors</u> affecting thinking and braking distance in <u>different situations</u>.

E.g. if a parent is driving her <u>children</u> to school <u>early</u> in the morning on an <u>autumn</u> day, her <u>thinking</u> distance could be affected by <u>tiredness</u>, or by her children <u>distracting</u> her. Her <u>braking</u> distance could be affected by <u>ice</u>, or by <u>leaves</u> on the road reducing the <u>friction</u>/grip.

Stopping distance = thinking distance + braking distance...

The exam might ask you to give factors, <u>other than speed</u>, which affect <u>thinking</u> or <u>braking</u> distances, so make sure you know <u>all the factors</u> that affect each of these and <u>what their effects are</u>.

Stopping Safely

Plotting a graph is always handy when there's a lot of info to take in. These <u>velocity/time graphs</u> illustrate really clearly how high speeds affect both <u>thinking and braking distances</u>.

Thinking and Braking Distance can be Seen on *v/t* Graphs

The <u>graph</u> below shows the <u>velocity</u> of a vehicle as the driver performs an emergency stop.

See p.23 for more on v/t graphs.

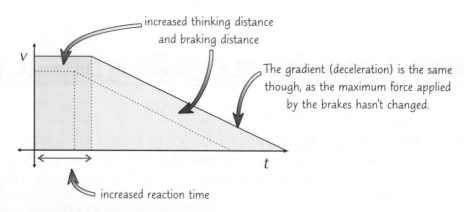

brakes applied

This area gives the thinking distance.

This area gives the braking distance.

v

t

reaction time

But if the driver is going <u>faster</u>, and he's a bit <u>tired</u>....

increased thinking distance and braking distance

The gradient (deceleration) is the same though, as the maximum force applied by the brakes hasn't changed.

v

t

increased reaction time

Large Decelerations can be **Dangerous**

1) <u>Large decelerations</u> of objects and people (e.g. in car crashes) can cause <u>serious injuries</u>. This is because a large deceleration requires a <u>large force</u> — $F = m \times a$.

2) The <u>force</u> can be <u>lowered</u> by <u>slowing</u> the object down over a <u>longer time</u>, i.e. decreasing its deceleration.

3) <u>Safety features</u> in vehicles are designed to <u>increase collision times</u>, which <u>reduces</u> the <u>force</u>, and so reduces the risk of injury. For example, <u>seat belts stretch</u> slightly and <u>air bags</u> slow you down gradually. <u>Crumple zones</u> are areas at the front and back of a vehicle which <u>crumple up easily</u> in a collision, increasing the time taken to stop.

> **EXAMPLE:** **Estimate the resultant force acting on a car stopping quickly from 15 m/s.**
>
> 1) Estimate the <u>deceleration</u> of the car — you did that for this example on page 20.
>
> 2) <u>Estimate</u> the <u>mass</u> of the car.
>
> 3) Put these numbers into <u>Newton's 2nd Law</u>.
>
> The car comes to a stop in ~1 s.
> $a = (v - u) \div t = (0 - 15) \div 1 = -15$ m/s^2
>
> Mass of a car is ~1000 kg.
>
> $F = m \times a$
>
> $= 1000 \times -15 = -15\ 000$ N
>
> The force here is negative as it acts in the opposite direction to the motion of the car.

4) The brakes of a vehicle <u>do work</u> on its wheels (see p.85). This <u>transfers energy</u> from the vehicle's <u>kinetic energy store</u> to the <u>thermal energy store</u> of the <u>brakes</u>. Very large decelerations may cause the brakes to <u>overheat</u> (so they don't work as well). They could also cause the vehicle to <u>skid</u>.

Warm-Up & Exam Questions

Time to apply the brakes for a second and put your brain through an MOT. Try out these questions. If you can handle these, your exam should be clear of hazards.

Warm-Up Questions

1) Describe an experiment you could carry out, using a ruler, to measure the reaction time of an individual.

2) What is meant by 'thinking distance'?

3) What must be added to the thinking distance to find the total stopping distance of a car?

4) Give an example of how poor weather can affect a driver's ability to stop a car before hitting a hazard.

5) Explain how crumple zones reduce the risk of harm in a car crash.

Exam Question

1   **Figure 1** shows how thinking distance and stopping distance vary with speed for a car travelling on a clear day on a dry road.

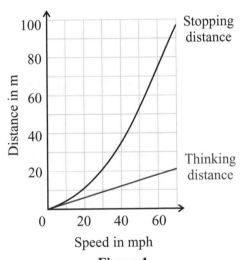

Figure 1

(a) Use **Figure 1** to determine the braking distance for a car travelling at 40 mph.

[3 marks]

(b) Using **Figure 1**, determine whether the thinking distance or braking distance is greater at 50 miles per hour.

[1 mark]

(c) Using **Figure 1**, determine whether stopping distance is directly proportional to speed. Explain your answer.

[1 mark]

(d) Describe how the shape of each of the graphs on **Figure 1** would change if the data was taken for the same driver travelling on an icy road.

[2 marks]

Revision Summary for Section 1

That wraps up <u>Section 1</u> — time to put yourself to the test and find out <u>how much you really know</u>.
- Try these questions and <u>tick off each one</u> when you <u>get it right</u>.
- When you've done <u>all the questions</u> under a heading and are <u>completely happy</u> with it, tick it off.

Motion (p.18-23) ☑

1) What is the difference between a scalar and a vector quantity? Give two examples of each. ☑
2) Give the equation relating distance travelled, speed and time. ☑
3) Estimate typical speeds for...
   a) ... walking...
   b) ... cycling...
   c) ... a car in a built-up area. ☑
4) Suggest appropriate equipment for measuring a person's walking speed. ☑
5) Define acceleration in terms of velocity and time. ☑
6) What is the value of acceleration due to gravity near the Earth's surface? ☑
7) What does the gradient represent on
   a) ... a distance/time graph?
   b) ... a velocity/time graph? ☑
8) How would you find the distance travelled by an object from its velocity/time graph? ☑

Newton's Laws, Forces and Momentum (p.25-34) ☑

9) State Newton's First and Second Laws of Motion. ☑
10) Explain why there must be a force acting to produce circular motion. What is the name of the force? ☑
11) What is inertial mass? ☑
12) What is Newton's Third Law of Motion? Give an example of it in action. ☑
13) What piece of equipment is appropriate for measuring the speed of a trolley rolling down a ramp? ☑
14) What is the formula for calculating the weight of an object? ☑
15) State the formula used to calculate an object's momentum. ☑
16) True or false? For an object's momentum to change more quickly,
    a greater force on the object is needed. ☑

Reaction Times and Car Safety (p.36-38) ☑

17) What is meant by a person's reaction time? ☑
18) State two factors that can affect the thinking distance for a stopping car. ☑
19) State four things that can affect the braking distance of a vehicle. ☑
20) Explain why cars have safety features to reduce the decelerations experienced by passengers. ☑

Energy Stores

Energy is <u>never used up</u>. Instead it's just <u>transferred</u> between different <u>energy stores</u> and different objects...

Energy Exists in **Stores**

Energy can be transferred between and held in different <u>energy stores</u>. There are eight you need to know:

<u>Thermal</u> — any object — the <u>hotter</u> it is, the <u>more</u> energy it has in this <u>store</u>.
<u>Kinetic</u> — anything <u>moving</u> has energy in this store (see below).
<u>Gravitational potential</u> — anything in a <u>gravitational field</u> (i.e. anything that can <u>fall</u>) (see below).
<u>Elastic potential</u> — anything <u>stretched</u>, like springs, rubber bands, etc. (p.132).
<u>Chemical</u> — anything that can release energy by a <u>chemical reaction</u>, e.g. food, fuels.
<u>Magnetic</u> — e.g. two <u>magnets</u> that attract and repel each other.
<u>Electrostatic</u> — e.g. two <u>charges</u> that attract and repel each other.
<u>Nuclear</u> — <u>atomic nuclei</u> release energy from this store in <u>nuclear reactions</u>.

Movement Means Energy in an Object's **Kinetic Energy Store**

1) Anything that is <u>moving</u> has energy in its <u>kinetic energy store</u>. Energy is transferred <u>to</u> this store when an object <u>speeds up</u> and is transferred <u>away</u> from this store when an object <u>slows down</u>.

2) The energy in the <u>kinetic energy store</u> depends on the object's <u>mass</u> and <u>speed</u>. The <u>greater its mass</u> and the <u>faster</u> it's going, the <u>more energy</u> there will be in its kinetic energy store.

3) There's a <u>slightly tricky</u> formula for it, so you have to concentrate <u>a little bit harder</u> for this one.

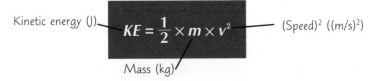

Kinetic energy (J) ─── $$KE = \frac{1}{2} \times m \times v^2$$ ─── (Speed)^2 ((m/s)^2)

Mass (kg)

EXAMPLE:

A car of mass 2500 kg is travelling at 20 m/s. Calculate the energy in its kinetic energy store.

$KE = \frac{1}{2} \times m \times v^2 = \frac{1}{2} \times 2500 \times 20^2 = 500\ 000$ J

Raised Objects Store Energy in **Gravitational Potential** Energy Stores

1) <u>Lifting</u> an object in a <u>gravitational field</u> causes a <u>transfer of energy</u> to the <u>gravitational potential energy</u> (g.p.e.) store of the raised object. The <u>higher</u> the object is lifted, the <u>more</u> energy is transferred to this store.

2) The amount of energy in a gravitational potential energy store depends on the object's <u>mass</u>, its <u>height</u> and the <u>strength</u> of the gravitational field the object is in.

3) You can use this equation to find the <u>change in energy</u> in an object's gravitational potential energy store for a <u>change in vertical height</u>, Δh.

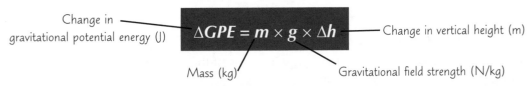

Change in gravitational potential energy (J) ─── $$\Delta GPE = m \times g \times \Delta h$$ ─── Change in vertical height (m)

Mass (kg) Gravitational field strength (N/kg)

Energy Stores and Transfers

Now you know about the different energy stores, it's time to find out how energy is <u>transferred</u> between them.

Energy is **Never Created** or **Destroyed**

This is a <u>really important</u> principle in physics, it is called <u>conservation of energy</u>:

> <u>Energy</u> can be <u>stored</u>, <u>transferred</u> between <u>stores</u>, and <u>dissipated</u>, but it can never be <u>created or destroyed</u>.

See page 45 for more on dissipation.

The **Total Energy** of a **Closed System** Doesn't Change

1) A <u>closed system</u> is just a system (a collection of objects) that can be treated <u>completely on its own</u>. The <u>total energy</u> of a closed system has <u>no net change</u>.

2) If you get a question where the energy of a system <u>increases</u> or <u>decreases</u>, then it's <u>not closed</u>.

3) But you can <u>make it into a closed system</u> by <u>increasing the number of things</u> you treat as part of it.

> For example, a <u>pan of water</u> heating on a hob <u>isn't</u> a closed system, but the <u>pan</u>, the <u>gas</u> and the <u>oxygen</u> that burn to heat it, and <u>their surroundings</u> (e.g. if they're in a perfectly insulated room) are a <u>closed system</u>.

You Need to Identify **Different Types** of **Energy Transfer**

1) When a system <u>changes</u>, <u>energy is transferred</u>. Energy is <u>transferred</u> in <u>four different ways</u>:

- <u>Mechanically</u> — a <u>force</u> acting on an object (and doing <u>work</u>, p.85), e.g. pushing, stretching, squashing.
- <u>Electrically</u> — a <u>charge</u> doing <u>work</u> (p.95), e.g. charges moving round a circuit.
- <u>By heating</u> — energy transferred from a <u>hotter</u> object to a <u>colder</u> object, e.g. heating a pan on a hob.
- <u>By radiation</u> — energy transferred by <u>waves</u>, e.g. energy from the Sun reaching Earth by light.

2) You need to be able to describe how <u>energy</u> gets <u>transferred</u> from <u>store to store</u>. Here's one <u>example</u> (there's more on the next page):

> <u>A ball rolling up a slope</u>
>
> The ball <u>does work</u> against the gravitational force, so energy is transferred <u>mechanically</u> from the <u>kinetic energy store</u> of the ball to its <u>gravitational potential energy store</u>.

Before: the ball has energy in it's kinetic energy store.

After: energy has been transferred to the ball's gravitational potential energy store.

No matter what store it's in, it's all energy...

In the exam, make sure you refer to <u>energy</u> in terms of the <u>store</u> it's in. For example, if you're describing energy in a <u>hot object</u>, say it 'has energy in its thermal energy store'.

Energy Stores and Transfers

You can keep track of complicated <u>energy transfers</u> much more easily if you draw a <u>diagram</u>.

More Examples of **Energy Transfers**

Here come a few more <u>examples</u> of everyday <u>energy transfers</u> that you need to get to grips with...

<u>A bat hitting a ball</u>

The bat has energy in its <u>kinetic energy store</u>. Some of this is transferred <u>mechanically</u> to the ball's <u>kinetic energy store</u>. Some energy is also transferred <u>mechanically</u> to the <u>thermal energy stores</u> of the bat and the ball (and to the <u>surroundings</u> by <u>heating</u>). The <u>rest</u> is carried away by <u>sound</u>.

<u>A rock dropped from a cliff</u>

Assuming there's <u>no air resistance</u>, <u>gravity</u> does work on the rock, so the rock constantly <u>accelerates</u> towards the ground. Energy is transferred <u>mechanically</u> from the rock's <u>gravitational potential</u> energy store to its <u>kinetic</u> energy store.

<u>A car slowing down (without braking)</u>

Energy in the <u>kinetic energy store</u> of the car is transferred <u>mechanically</u> (due to <u>friction</u> between the tyres and road), and then by <u>heating</u>, to the <u>thermal energy stores</u> of the car and road.

<u>A kettle boiling water</u>

Energy is transferred <u>electrically</u> from the mains to the heating element of the kettle, and then by <u>heating</u> to the <u>thermal energy store</u> of the water.

You can **Draw Diagrams** to Show Energy Transfers

Diagrams can make it <u>easier</u> to see <u>what's going on</u> when energy is transferred. The diagram below shows the energy transferred when a ball is thrown upwards, taking air resistance into account. The <u>boxes</u> represent <u>stores</u> and the <u>arrows</u> show <u>transfers</u>:

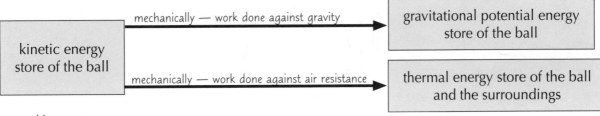

| kinetic energy store of the ball | mechanically — work done against gravity → | gravitational potential energy store of the ball |
| | mechanically — work done against air resistance → | thermal energy store of the ball and the surroundings |

You may have to use or draw a diagram like this in the exam, so make sure you understand what it's showing.

Energy is transferred between the different stores of objects...

Energy stores pop up <u>everywhere</u> in physics. You need to be able to describe <u>how energy is transferred</u>, and <u>which stores</u> it gets transferred between, for <u>any scenario</u>. So, it's time to make sure you know all the <u>energy stores</u> and <u>transfer methods</u> like the back of your hand.

Warm-Up & Exam Questions

These questions give you chance to use your knowledge about energy stores and energy transfers.

Warm-Up Questions

1) State the equation that links energy in an object's kinetic energy store with mass and speed.
2) Which has more energy in its kinetic energy store: a person walking at 3 miles per hour, or a lorry travelling at 60 miles per hour?
3) Give two methods of energy transfer.
4) Describe the main energy transfer that takes place when the sun warms a glass of water.

Exam Questions

1   A motor lifts a load of mass 20 kg.
    The load gains 140 J of energy in its gravitational potential energy store.

   (a)   State the equation that links change in gravitational potential energy, mass, gravitational field strength and change in vertical height.

         Use this equation to calculate the height through which the motor lifts the load.
         Assume the gravitational field strength = 10 N/kg.

         [4 marks]

   (b)   The motor releases the load and the load falls.
         Ignoring air resistance, describe the changes in the way energy is stored that take place as the load falls.

         [2 marks]

   (c)   Describe how your answer to (b) would differ if air resistance was not ignored.

         [1 mark]

2   A sling-shot is used to catapult a 60 g rock directly upwards.
    Figure 1 shows how the rock's height changes over time.

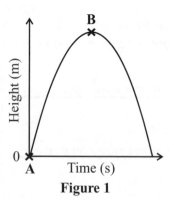

Figure 1

   (a)   From launch (**A**) to the peak of the rock's flight (**B**), describe how energy is transferred.

         [3 marks]

   (b)   Initially, the speed of the rock is 18 m/s.
         Calculate the amount of energy in the rock's kinetic energy store at this time.

         [2 marks]

   (c)   Use your answer to (b) to calculate the height of the rock at **B**.

         [3 marks]

Unwanted Energy Transfers

So energy is <u>transferred</u> between different <u>stores</u>. But not all of the energy is transferred to <u>useful</u> stores.

Most **Energy Transfers** Involve Some **Losses**, Often by **Heating**

1) You've already met the <u>principle of conservation of energy</u> on page 42, but another <u>important principle</u> you need to know is:

> Energy is <u>only useful</u> when it is <u>transferred</u> from one store to a <u>useful store</u>.

2) <u>Useful devices</u> can <u>transfer energy</u> from <u>one store</u> to a <u>useful store</u>.

3) However, some of the <u>input energy</u> is always <u>dissipated or wasted</u>, often to <u>thermal energy stores</u> of the surroundings.

Dissipated is a fancy way of saying the energy is spread out and so is 'lost'.

4) Whenever work is done <u>mechanically</u> (see p.42), <u>frictional forces</u> have to be overcome, including things like <u>moving parts rubbing</u> together, and <u>air resistance</u>. The energy needed to overcome these frictional forces is transferred to the <u>thermal energy stores</u> of whatever's doing the work and the <u>surroundings</u>.

5) This energy usually <u>isn't useful</u>, and is <u>quickly dissipated</u>.

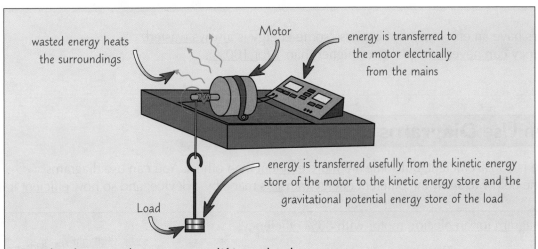

- The diagram shows a <u>motor</u> lifting a load.
- The motor transfers energy usefully from its <u>kinetic energy store</u> to the <u>kinetic</u> energy store and the <u>gravitational potential</u> energy store of the <u>load</u>.
- But it also transfers energy <u>mechanically</u> to the <u>thermal energy stores</u> of its moving parts, and <u>electrically</u> to the <u>thermal energy stores</u> of its <u>circuits</u>.
- This energy is <u>dissipated</u>, heating the surroundings.

6) The conservation of energy principle means that:
<u>total energy input = useful energy output + wasted energy</u>.

7) The <u>less energy</u> that's <u>wasted</u>, the <u>more efficient</u> the device is said to be. The amount of energy that's wasted can often be <u>reduced</u> — see page 47.

Before you know what's waste, you've got to know what's useful...

If you're trying to work out <u>how</u> a device is <u>wasting energy</u>, the first thing you should do is figure out which store is <u>useful</u>. For example, for a <u>phone charger</u>, only energy transferred to the <u>chemical energy store</u> of the phone's battery is <u>useful</u>. Then you know energy that ends up <u>anywhere else</u> is <u>wasted</u>.

Efficiency

Devices have energy transferred to them, but only transfer some of that energy to useful energy stores. Wouldn't it be great if we could tell how much the device usefully transfers? That's where efficiency comes in.

You can **Calculate** the **Efficiency** of an **Energy Transfer**

The efficiency of any device is defined as:

$$\text{efficiency} = \frac{\text{useful energy transferred by the device (J)}}{\text{total energy supplied to the device (J)}}$$

This will give the efficiency as a decimal. To give it as a percentage, you need to multiply the answer by 100.

EXAMPLE:

A toaster transfers 216 000 J of energy electrically from the mains. 84 000 J of energy is transferred to the bread's thermal energy store. Calculate the efficiency of the toaster.

This could also be written as 39% (to 2 s.f.).

$$\text{efficiency} = \frac{\text{useful energy transferred by the device}}{\text{total energy supplied to the device}} = \frac{84\,000}{216\,000} = 0.388... = 0.39 \text{ (to 2 s.f.)}$$

All devices have an efficiency, but because some energy is always wasted, the efficiency can never be equal to or higher than 1 (or 100%).

You can Use **Diagrams** to Show **Efficiency**

No device is 100% efficient, but some are more efficient than others. You can use diagrams like the one below to show the different energy transfers made by a device, and so how efficient it is:

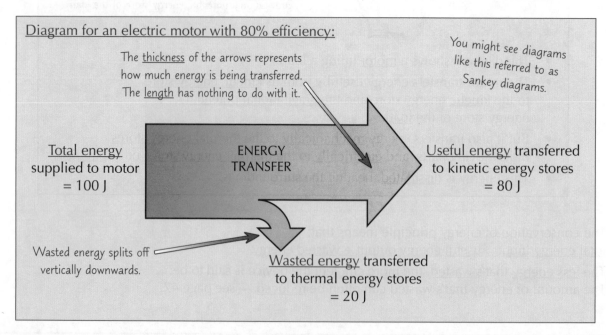

Diagram for an electric motor with 80% efficiency:

The thickness of the arrows represents how much energy is being transferred. The length has nothing to do with it.

You might see diagrams like this referred to as Sankey diagrams.

Total energy supplied to motor = 100 J

ENERGY TRANSFER

Useful energy transferred to kinetic energy stores = 80 J

Wasted energy splits off vertically downwards.

Wasted energy transferred to thermal energy stores = 20 J

You can reduce the amount of energy that's wasted in various ways — including by lubrication and by thermal insulation. Decreasing the amount of wasted energy means that a higher proportion of the supplied energy is transferred to useful stores, so the efficiency of the process is increased.

Reducing Unwanted Energy Transfers

There are a few ways you can <u>reduce</u> the amount of energy scampering off to a <u>completely useless</u> store — <u>lubrication</u> and <u>thermal insulation</u> are the ones you need to know about. Read on to find out more...

Lubrication Reduces Energy Transferred by Friction

1) Whenever something <u>moves</u>, there's usually at least one <u>frictional force</u> acting against it.

2) This <u>transfers</u> energy <u>mechanically</u> (<u>work</u> is done <u>against</u> friction) to the <u>thermal energy store</u> of the objects involved, which is then <u>dissipated</u> by heating to the surroundings.

3) For example, <u>pushing</u> a <u>box</u> along the <u>ground</u> causes energy to be transferred mechanically to the thermal energy stores of the box and the ground. This energy is then <u>radiated away</u> to the thermal energy store of the surroundings.

For objects that are touching each other, <u>lubricants</u> can be used to reduce the friction between the objects' surfaces when they move.

Lubricants are usually <u>liquids</u> (like <u>oil</u>), so they can <u>flow</u> easily between objects and <u>coat</u> them.

Insulation Reduces the Rate of Energy Transfer by Heating

1) When one side of an object is <u>heated</u>, the particles in the <u>hotter</u> part <u>vibrate</u> more and <u>collide</u> with each other. This transfers energy from their <u>kinetic energy stores</u> to <u>other particles</u>, which then vibrate faster.

2) This process is called <u>conduction</u>. It <u>transfers energy</u> through the object.

3) All materials have a <u>thermal conductivity</u> — it describes how well a material transfers energy by conduction. For example, <u>metals</u> have a <u>high thermal conductivity</u> and <u>gases</u> (like <u>air</u>) have a <u>low thermal conductivity</u>.

4) To <u>reduce</u> a building's <u>rate of cooling</u>, walls should be <u>thick</u> and have <u>low thermal conductivity</u>.

5) You can also use <u>thermal insulation</u> in buildings:

1) Some houses have <u>cavity walls</u>, made up of an <u>inner</u> and an <u>outer</u> wall with an air gap in the middle. The <u>air gap</u> reduces the amount of energy transferred by conduction through the walls.

2) <u>Loft insulation</u> can be laid out across the loft floor and ceiling. Fibreglass wool is often used which is a <u>good insulator</u> as it has pockets of trapped air. Loft insulation reduces energy loss by <u>conduction</u>.

3) <u>Double-glazed windows</u> work in the same way as cavity walls — they have an air gap between two sheets of glass to prevent energy transfer by <u>conduction</u> through the windows.

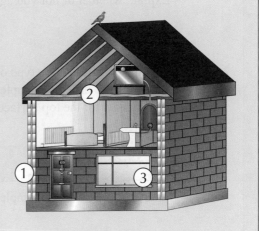

Having a well-insulated house can reduce your heating bills...

When people talk of <u>energy loss</u>, it's <u>not</u> that the energy has disappeared. It still exists (see <u>conservation of energy</u> on page 42), just not in the <u>store</u> we want. For example, in a car, you want the energy to transfer to the <u>kinetic energy store</u> of the wheels, and not to the <u>thermal energy stores</u> of the moving components.

Warm-Up & Exam Questions

Don't let your energy dissipate. These questions will let you see how efficient your revision has been.

Warm-Up Questions

1) Which energy store does wasted energy typically end up in?
2) Why is the efficiency of an appliance always less than 100%?
3) Give one way you could reduce the frictional forces in the hinge of an automatic door.
4) For a given material, how does its thermal conductivity affect the rate of energy transfer through it?
5) How does the thickness of a building's walls affect the building's rate of cooling?

Exam Questions

1 Torch A transfers 1200 J of energy per minute.
480 J of this is transferred away usefully as light, 690 J is transferred
to useless thermal energy stores and 30 J is transferred away as sound.

    (a) Write down the equation linking efficiency, useful energy transferred by the device
and total energy supplied to the device.

[1 mark]

    (b) Calculate the efficiency of torch A.

[2 marks]

Torch B transfers 10 J of energy away usefully as light each second.

    (c) Torch B has an efficiency of 0.55. Calculate the total energy supplied to torch B each second.

[3 marks]

    (d) Each torch is powered by an identical battery. A student claims that the battery in torch B will
go 'flat' quicker than in torch A because it transfers more energy away as light each minute.
Explain whether or not you agree with the student.

[1 mark]

2 A student investigates which type of window is the best at reducing unwanted energy transfers.
The student places different samples of windows on a hot plate and measures
how long it takes for the top surface of the window sample to reach 30 °C.

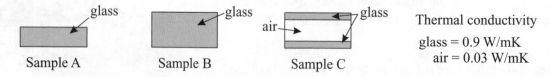

Figure 1

Figure 1 shows the cross-sections of each window sample. Rank them from best to worst for reducing
unwanted energy transfers from a house and explain your choices.

[4 marks]

Energy Resources

There are lots of <u>energy resources</u> available on Earth. They are either <u>renewable</u> or <u>non-renewable</u> resources.

Non-Renewable Energy Resources Will Run Out One Day

<u>Non-renewable</u> energy resources are <u>fossil fuels</u> and <u>nuclear fuel</u> (e.g. uranium and plutonium). <u>Fossil fuels</u> are natural resources that form <u>underground</u> over <u>millions</u> of years. They are typically <u>burnt</u> to provide energy. The <u>three main</u> fossil fuels are:

1) Coal
2) Oil
3) (Natural) Gas

- These will <u>all</u> 'run out' one day.
- They all do <u>damage</u> to the environment.
- But they provide <u>most of our energy</u>.

Renewable Energy Resources Will Never Run Out

<u>Renewable</u> energy resources include:

1) The Sun (Solar)
2) Wind
3) Hydro-electricity
4) Bio-fuel
5) Tides

- These will <u>never run out</u> — the energy can be '<u>renewed</u>' as it is used.
- Most of them do <u>damage</u> the environment, but in <u>less nasty</u> ways than non-renewables.
- The trouble is they <u>don't</u> provide much <u>energy</u> and some of them are <u>unreliable</u> because they depend on the weather.

Solar Cells — Expensive but No Environmental Damage

1) Solar cells are made from <u>materials</u> that use energy <u>transferred</u> by <u>light</u> to create an <u>electric current</u>.
2) Solar power is often used in <u>remote places</u> where there's not much choice (e.g. the Australian outback) and to power electric <u>road signs</u> and <u>satellites</u>.
3) There's <u>no pollution</u>. (Although they do require quite a lot of <u>energy</u> to <u>make</u>.)
4) <u>Initial costs</u> are <u>high</u>, but there are basically <u>no running costs</u>.
5) They're mainly used to generate electricity on a relatively <u>small scale</u>.
6) Solar power is best in <u>sunny countries</u>, but it can be used in <u>cloudy countries</u> like Britain.
7) You <u>can't</u> make solar power at <u>night</u> or <u>increase production</u> when there's extra demand.

Wind Power — Lots of Little Wind Turbines

1) Each wind turbine has a <u>generator</u> inside it — wind rotates the <u>blades</u>, which turn the generator and produce <u>electricity</u>. So there's <u>no pollution</u>.
2) <u>Initial costs</u> are quite <u>high</u>, but <u>running</u> costs are <u>minimal</u>.
3) But <u>lots</u> of them are needed to produce as much <u>power</u> as, for example, a <u>coal</u> power plant. This means they can <u>spoil the view</u>. They can also be <u>noisy</u>, which can be annoying for people living nearby.
4) They <u>only</u> work when it's <u>windy</u>, so you can't always <u>supply</u> electricity, or respond to <u>high demand</u>.

More Renewable Energy Resources

Bio-fuels, hydro-electricity and tidal barrages — three more energy resources to get your head around.

Bio-fuels are Made from Plants and Waste

1) Bio-fuels are renewable energy resources created from either plant products or animal dung. They can be solid, liquid or gas and can be burnt to produce electricity or run cars.

2) They are supposedly carbon neutral, although there is some debate about this as it's only really true if you keep growing plants (or raising animals) at the rate that you're burning things.

3) Bio-fuels are fairly reliable, as crops take a relatively short time to grow and different crops can be grown all year round. However, they cannot respond to immediate energy demands. To combat this, bio-fuels are continuously produced and stored for when they are needed.

4) The cost to refine bio-fuels is very high. Also, some worry that growing crops specifically for bio-fuels will mean there isn't enough space or water for crops that are grown for food.

5) In some regions, large areas of forest have been cleared to make room to grow bio-fuels, resulting in lots of species losing their natural habitats. The decay or burning of this cleared vegetation also increases methane and CO_2 emissions.

Hydro-electricity — Building Dams and Flooding Valleys

1) Producing hydro-electricity usually involves flooding a valley by building a big dam. Rainwater is caught and allowed out through turbines. There is no pollution (as such).

2) There is a big impact on the environment due to the flooding of the valley and possible loss of habitat for some species.

3) A big advantage is it can immediately respond to increased electricity demand — more water can be let out through the turbines to generate more electricity.

4) Initial costs are often high but there are minimal running costs and it's generally a reliable energy source.

Tidal Barrages — Using the Sun and Moon's Gravity

1) Tidal barrages are big dams built across river estuaries with turbines in them.

2) As the tide comes in it fills up the estuary. The water is then let out through turbines at a controlled speed to generate electricity.

3) There is no pollution but they affect boat access, can spoil the view and they alter the habitat for wildlife, e.g. wading birds.

4) Tides are pretty reliable (they're caused by the Sun and Moon's gravity and always happen twice a day). But the height of the tides is variable and barrages don't work when the water level is the same either side.

5) Initial costs are moderately high, but there are no fuel costs and minimal running costs.

Non-Renewable Resources

Renewable resources may sound like great news for the environment. But when it comes down to it, they don't currently meet all our needs so we still need those nasty, polluting non-renewables.

Non-Renewables are Reliable and Cost Effective...

1) Fossil fuels and nuclear energy are reliable. There's enough fossil and nuclear fuels to meet current demand, and they are extracted from the Earth at a fast enough rate that power plants always have fuel in stock. This means that the power plants can respond quickly to changes in demand.

2) While the set-up costs of power plants can be quite high compared to some other energy resources, the running costs aren't that expensive. Combined with fairly low fuel extraction costs, using fossil fuels is a cost effective way to produce energy (which is why it's so popular).

...But Create Other Problems

1) Coal, oil and gas release carbon dioxide (CO_2) into the atmosphere when they're burned. All this CO_2 adds to the greenhouse effect, and contributes to global warming.

2) Burning coal and oil also releases sulfur dioxide, which causes acid rain — which can be harmful to trees and soils and can have far-reaching effects in ecosystems.

3) Acid rain can be reduced by taking the sulfur out before the fuel is burned, or cleaning up the emissions.

4) Views can be spoilt by fossil fuel power plants, and coal mining makes a mess of the landscape, especially "open-cast mining".

5) Oil spillages cause serious environmental problems, affecting mammals and birds that live in and around the sea. We try to avoid them, but they'll always happen.

6) Nuclear power is clean, since it does not directly release CO_2, but the nuclear waste is very dangerous and difficult to dispose of.

Radiation can be very dangerous to humans — see p.80 for more.

7) Nuclear fuel (e.g. uranium or plutonium) is relatively cheap but the overall cost of nuclear power is high due to the cost of the power plant and final decommissioning.

8) Nuclear power always carries the risk of a major catastrophe like the Fukushima disaster in Japan.

Trends in Energy Resource Use

Over time, the types of energy resources we use change. There are lots of reasons for this — breakthroughs in technology, understanding more about how they affect the environment or changes in cost are just a few.

Currently We Depend on Fossil Fuels

1) Over the 20th century, the electricity use of the UK hugely increased as the population grew and people began to use electricity for more and more things.

2) Since the beginning of the 21st century, electricity use in the UK has been decreasing (slowly), as we make appliances more efficient (p.46) and become more careful with energy use in our homes.

3) Most of our electricity is produced using fossil fuels (mostly coal and gas) and from nuclear power.

4) Generating electricity isn't the only reason we burn fossil fuels — oil (diesel and petrol) is used to fuel cars, and gas is used to heat homes and cook food.

5) However, renewable energy resources can be used for these purposes as well. Bio-fuels can be used to exclusively power vehicles, and solar water heaters can be used to heat buildings.

The Aim is to Increase Renewable Energy Use

1) Burning fossil fuels has a lot of negative effects on the environment (p.51). This has led to many people wanting to use more renewable energy resources that have less of an effect on the environment.

2) Pressure from other countries and the public has meant that governments have begun to introduce targets for using renewable resources. This in turn puts pressure on energy providers to build new power plants that use renewable resources to make sure they do not lose business and money.

3) Car companies have also been affected by this change in attitude towards the environment. Electric cars and hybrids (cars powered by two fuels, e.g. petrol and electricity) are increasing in popularity.

The Use of Renewables is Usually Limited by Reliability and Money

1) Building new renewable power plants costs money, so some smaller energy providers are reluctant to do this — especially when fossil fuels are such a cost effective way of meeting demand.

2) Even if new power plants are built, there are a lot of arguments over where they should be. E.g. many people don't want to live next to a wind farm, which can lead to protests.

3) Energy resources like wind power are not as reliable as traditional fossil fuels, whilst others cannot increase their power output on demand. This would mean either having to use a combination of different power plants (which would be expensive) or researching ways to improve reliability.

4) Research into improving the reliability and cost of renewable resources takes time and money. This means that, even with funding, it might be years before improvements are made. In the meantime, dependable, non-renewable power stations have to be used.

5) Making personal changes can also be quite expensive. Hybrid cars are generally more expensive than equivalent petrol cars and things like solar panels for your home are still quite pricey. The cost of these things is slowly going down, but they are still not an option for many people.

Going green is on-trend this season...

So with some people wanting to help the environment, others not wanting to be inconvenienced, and greener alternatives being expensive to set up, the energy resources we use are changing. Just not particularly quickly.

Warm-Up & Exam Questions

This is the last set of warm-up and exam questions on Section 2. They're not *too* horrendous, I promise.

Warm-Up Questions

1) Name three non-renewable energy resources.
2) Give one advantage and one disadvantage associated with solar power.
3) Give two ways in which using coal as an energy resource causes environmental problems.
4) Suggest two reasons why we can't just stop using fossil fuels immediately.

Exam Questions

1   The government of a country needs to generate more electricity to support a growing population. They want to use renewable energy resources in order to achieve this.

   (a)   The government has considered using wind, tides and hydro-electric power to generate electricity. Suggest **two** other renewable energy resources they could use.

[2 marks]

   (b)   In hydro-electric power stations, such as the one shown in **Figure 1**, water is held back behind a dam before being allowed to flow out through turbines.

       Give **one** environmental impact the government might be concerned about if they chose hydro-electric power to generate electricity.

[1 mark]

Figure 1

   (c)   The government choose to generate electricity using tidal barrages. Give **one** environmental advantage of generating electricity using tidal barrages.

[1 mark]

2   A family want to install solar panels on their roof. They have 8 m^2 of space on their roof for the solar panels. They use 32 500 000 J of energy per day. A 1 m^2 solar panel has an output of 200 J each second in good sunlight.

   (a)   Calculate the minimum number of 1 m^2 solar panels required to cover the family's daily energy use, assuming there are 5 hours of good sunlight in a day.

[4 marks]

   (b)   Determine, using your answer from (a), whether the family can install enough solar panels to provide all of the energy they use, assuming there are 5 hours of good sunlight every day.

[1 mark]

   (c)   In reality, the number of hours of good sunlight in a day varies based on the weather and time of year. Discuss the reliability of energy from solar panels compared to from a local coal-fired power station.

[3 marks]

Revision Summary for Section 2

Well, that's that for <u>Section 2</u> — this is when you find out <u>how much of it went in</u>.
- Try these questions and <u>tick off each one</u> when you <u>get it right</u>.
- When you've done <u>all the questions</u> under a heading and are <u>completely happy</u> with it, tick it off.

Energy Stores and Transfers (p.41-43) ☑

1) Write down four energy stores. ☑
2) What kind of energy store is energy transferred to when you compress a spring? ☑
3) If energy is transferred to an object's kinetic energy store, what happens to its speed? ☑
4) Give the equation for finding the change in an object's gravitational potential energy. ☑
5) True or false? Energy can be destroyed. ☑
6) What is a closed system? ☑
7) Give the name of the transfer in which energy moves from a hotter object to a cooler object. ☑
8) Describe the energy transfers that occur when an electric kettle boils water. ☑

Reducing Unwanted Energy Transfers and Improving Efficiency (p.45-47) ☑

9) Explain what is meant by the term 'dissipate'. ☑
10) True or false? It is possible to manufacture appliances with an efficiency greater than 1. ☑
11) How can you reduce unwanted energy transfers in a machine with moving components? ☑
12) True or false? A high thermal conductivity means there is a high rate of energy transfer. ☑
13) True or false? Thicker walls make a house cool down quicker. ☑
14) Give three ways to prevent unwanted energy transfers in a home. ☑

Energy Resources and Trends in their Use (p.49-52) ☑

15) Name four renewable energy resources. ☑
16) What is the difference between renewable and non-renewable energy resources? ☑
17) Give one advantage and one disadvantage associated with generating electricity using wind power. ☑
18) Give one potential environmental impact of bio-fuels. ☑
19) Give one environmental benefit of using nuclear power. ☑
20) Explain why the UK plans to use more renewable energy resources in the future. ☑

Wave Basics

Waves <u>transfer energy</u> from one place to another <u>without</u> transferring any <u>matter</u> (stuff).

Energy and Information are Transferred by Waves

1) <u>Waves</u> transfer <u>energy</u> and <u>information</u> in the <u>direction</u> they are <u>travelling</u>.

2) When waves travel through a medium, the <u>particles</u> of the medium <u>vibrate</u> and <u>transfer energy and information</u> between each other.

3) But overall, the particles stay in the <u>same place</u> — <u>only energy and information</u> are transferred.

> For example, if you drop a twig into a calm pool of water, <u>ripples</u> form on the water's surface. The ripples <u>don't</u> carry the <u>water</u> (or the twig) away with them though.
>
> Similarly, if you strum a <u>guitar string</u> and create <u>sound waves</u>, the sound waves don't carry the <u>air</u> away from the guitar and create a <u>vacuum</u>.

Waves have Amplitude, Wavelength and Frequency

1) The <u>amplitude</u> of a wave is the <u>displacement</u> from the <u>rest position</u> to a <u>crest</u> or <u>trough</u>.

2) The <u>wavelength</u> is the length of a <u>full cycle</u> of the wave, e.g. from <u>crest to crest</u> (see below) or from <u>compression</u> to <u>compression</u> (see the next page).

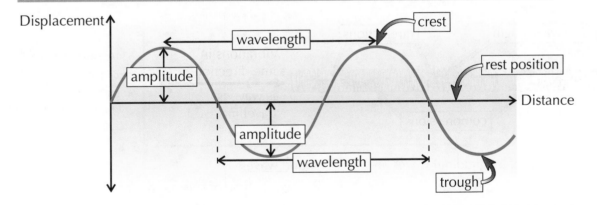

3) <u>Frequency</u> is the <u>number of complete cycles</u> of the wave passing a certain point <u>per second</u>. Frequency is measured in <u>hertz</u> (<u>Hz</u>). 1 Hz is <u>1 wave per second</u>.

4) The <u>period</u> of a wave is the <u>number of seconds</u> it takes for a <u>full cycle</u> of the wave to pass a point. Period = 1 ÷ frequency.

Waves only transfer energy and information...

It's <u>really</u> important that you understand this stuff <u>really</u> well, or the rest of this topic will simply be a blur. Make sure you can sketch the <u>wave diagram</u> above and can <u>label</u> all the features from memory.

Transverse and Longitudinal Waves

All waves are either <u>transverse</u> or <u>longitudinal</u>. Read on to find out more...

Transverse Waves Have Sideways Vibrations

1) In <u>transverse waves</u>, the vibrations are <u>perpendicular</u> (at 90°) to the <u>direction</u> the wave travels.

2) A spring wiggled <u>up and down</u> gives a <u>transverse wave</u>:

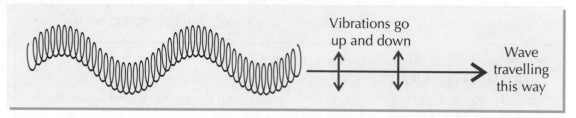

Vibrations go up and down

Wave travelling this way

3) <u>Most waves</u> are transverse, including:
   - <u>All electromagnetic waves</u>, e.g. light (p.63).
   - <u>S-waves</u> (a type of seismic wave).
   - <u>Ripples</u> and waves in <u>water</u> (see p.57).

Longitudinal Waves Have Parallel Vibrations

1) In <u>longitudinal waves</u>, the vibrations are <u>parallel</u> to the <u>direction</u> the wave travels.

2) Longitudinal waves <u>squash up</u> and <u>stretch out</u> the arrangement of particles in the medium they pass through, making <u>compressions</u> (<u>high pressure</u>, lots of particles) and <u>rarefactions</u> (<u>low pressure</u>, fewer particles).

3) If you <u>push</u> the end of a <u>spring</u>, you get a <u>longitudinal wave</u>:

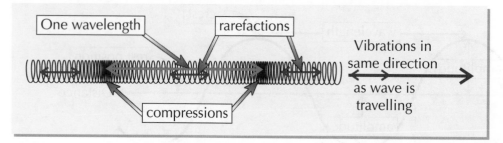

One wavelength   rarefactions

Vibrations in same direction as wave is travelling

compressions

A wavelength is still one complete cycle, e.g. from the middle of one compression to the middle of another.

4) Other examples of longitudinal waves are:
   - <u>Sound waves</u>.
   - <u>P-waves</u> (a type of seismic wave).

Wave Speed = Frequency × Wavelength

1) <u>Wave speed</u> is no different to any other speed — it tells you how <u>quickly</u> a <u>wave</u> moves through space.

2) There are <u>two</u> ways to calculate <u>wave speed</u>:

Wave speed (m/s) — $v = \dfrac{x}{t}$ — Distance (m), Time (s)

Wave speed (m/s) — $v = f \times \lambda$ — Wavelength (m), Frequency (Hz)

3) $v = f \times \lambda$ is sometimes referred to as '<u>the wave equation</u>'.

4) Remember, <u>velocity</u> is <u>speed</u> in a given <u>direction</u> (p.18). So, if you know the <u>direction</u> of a wave, you can use these equations to work out <u>wave velocity</u>.

Investigating Waves

The <u>speeds</u>, <u>frequencies</u> and <u>wavelengths</u> of waves can vary by huge amounts. So you have to use <u>suitable</u> <u>equipment</u> to measure waves in different materials, to make sure you get <u>accurate</u> and <u>precise</u> results.

Use an **Oscilloscope** to Measure the **Speed** of **Sound**

By attaching a <u>signal generator</u> to a speaker you can generate sounds with a specific <u>frequency</u>.
You can use <u>two microphones</u> and an <u>oscilloscope</u> to find the <u>wavelength</u> of the sound waves generated.

1) Set up the oscilloscope so the <u>detected waves</u> at each microphone are shown as <u>separate waves</u>.

2) Start with <u>both microphones</u> next to the speaker, then slowly <u>move one away</u> until the two waves are <u>aligned</u> on the display, but have moved <u>exactly one wavelength apart</u>.

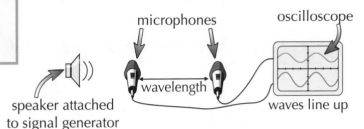

3) Measure the <u>distance between the microphones</u> to find one <u>wavelength</u> (λ).

4) You can then use the formula $\underline{v = f \times \lambda}$ (see previous page) to find the <u>speed</u> (v) of the <u>sound waves</u> passing through the <u>air</u> — the <u>frequency</u> (f) is whatever you set the <u>signal generator</u> to in the first place.

The speed of sound in air is around 340 m/s, so check your results roughly agree with this.

Measure the **Speed** of **Water Ripples** Using a **Strobe Light**

1) Using a <u>signal generator</u> attached to the <u>dipper</u> of a <u>ripple tank</u> you can create water waves at a <u>set frequency</u>.

2) Dim the lights and <u>turn on</u> the <u>strobe light</u> — you'll see a <u>wave pattern</u> made by the shadows of the <u>wave crests</u> on the screen below the tank.

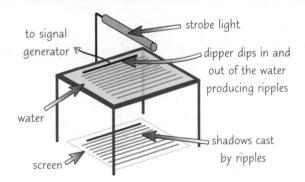

3) Alter the <u>frequency</u> of the <u>strobe light</u> until the wave pattern on the screen appears to '<u>freeze</u>' and stop moving. This happens when the frequency of the waves and the strobe light are <u>equal</u> — the waves appear <u>not to move</u> because they are being lit at the <u>same point</u> in their cycle <u>each time</u>.

4) The distance between each shadow line is equal to one wavelength. Measure the <u>distance</u> between lines that are 10 wavelengths apart, then find the <u>average wavelength</u>.

5) Use $v = f \times \lambda$ to calculate the <u>speed</u> of the waves.

If you don't know the frequency of the strobe light, you can find the frequency by using a regular light, so you can see the waves moving. Count how many waves pass a mark on the screen in a given time, then divide this by the time in seconds to find the frequency.

- Depending on the exact set-up of your apparatus, the waves seen on the screen may be <u>magnified</u>. In this case you'll need to work out the <u>scale factor</u> before you can find the <u>wavelength</u>.
- An easy way to do this it to stick a <u>piece of tape</u> of a <u>known length</u>, e.g. 10 cm, to the bottom of the ripple tank. Then <u>measure</u> the <u>length of its shadow</u>. If the shadow is <u>longer</u> than the tape, then what you're seeing on the screen is <u>magnified</u>.
- The length of the tape's shadow <u>divided</u> by the actual length of the tape will give the <u>scale factor</u>.

 **PRACTICAL**

Investigating Waves

There's one more <u>wave experiment</u> coming up. This time, it's to do with <u>waves in a solid</u>.

Use **Peak Frequency** to find the **Speed** of **Waves in Solids**

1) You can find the <u>speed of waves</u> in a <u>solid</u> by measuring the <u>frequency</u> of the <u>sound waves</u> produced when you hit the object, e.g. a rod, with a hammer.

2) Hitting the rod causes <u>waves</u> to be produced <u>along</u> the rod.

3) These waves make the rod <u>vibrate</u> and produce <u>sound waves</u> in the <u>air</u> around the rod (this is how a percussion triangle works).

4) These <u>sound waves</u> have the <u>same frequencies</u> as the waves <u>in the rod</u>.

5) Here is a <u>method</u> for measuring the <u>speed of waves</u> in a <u>metal rod</u>:

  • <u>Measure</u> and <u>record</u> the <u>length</u> of a <u>metal rod</u>, e.g. a brass rod.

  • Set up the apparatus shown in the diagram below, making sure to secure the rod at its <u>centre</u>.

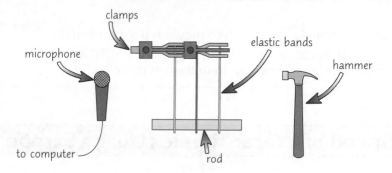

  • <u>Tap the rod</u> with the hammer. <u>Write down the peak frequency</u> displayed by the computer.

Lots of waves at lots of different frequencies are created in the rod when it is hit. The peak (loudest) frequency is created by this wave in the rod.

wave   rod

rod length = half a wavelength

  • <u>Repeat</u> this three times to get an <u>average peak frequency</u>.

  • Calculate the <u>speed</u> of the wave using $v = f \times \lambda$, where λ is equal to <u>twice the length</u> of the rod.

6) The <u>peak frequency</u> wave <u>always</u> has λ = rod length × 2, whatever the rod is made from. So this set-up is <u>suitable</u> for finding the wave speed in a rod of <u>any type of solid material</u>.

 PRACTICAL TIP

Learn the methods for all these practicals...

These experiments might seem quite different, but the <u>aim</u> in all of them is to try and find values for f and λ. All the experiments then use the <u>wave equation</u>, $v = f \times \lambda$, to calculate wave speed.

Warm-Up & Exam Questions

Now to check what's actually stuck in your mind over the last four pages...

Warm-Up Questions

1) A twig is dropped on a pool of water and creates water ripples.
   Explain why the twig stays where it is, rather than being carried away by the ripples.
2) What are the units of frequency?
3) Give one example of a longitudinal wave.
4) State the equation that relates wave speed, frequency and wavelength.

Exam Questions

1   **Figure 1** shows a graph of a water ripple.

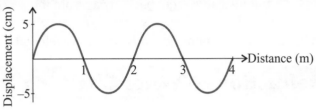

Figure 1

   (a) State whether water ripples
       are transverse or longitudinal.

       [1 mark]

   (b) Give the amplitude of this wave.

       [1 mark]

   (c) Find the wavelength of this wave.

       [1 mark]

   (d) If the frequency of the wave doubles but its speed stays
       the same, state what will happen to its wavelength.

       [1 mark]

PRACTICAL

2   **Figure 2** shows how an oscilloscope can be used to display sound waves by
   connecting microphones to it. Trace 1 shows the sound waves detected by
   microphone 1 and trace 2 shows the sound waves detected by microphone 2.

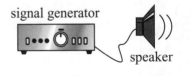 

Figure 2

   A student begins with both microphones at equal distances from the speaker and the signal generator set
   at a fixed frequency. He gradually moves microphone 2 away from the speaker, which causes trace 2 to
   move. He stops moving microphone 2 when both traces line up again as shown in **Figure 2**. He then
   measures the distance between the microphones.

   (a) Explain how his measurement could be used to work out the speed of sound in air.

       [2 marks]

   (b) With the frequency set to 50 Hz, the distance between the microphones was measured as 6.8 m.
       Calculate the speed of sound in air.

       [2 marks]

Wave Behaviour at Boundaries

How a wave behaves when it reaches a <u>boundary</u> depends on the <u>properties</u> of the <u>materials</u> either side of the boundary. It also depends on the <u>wavelength</u> of the wave.

Waves are **Absorbed, Transmitted** and **Reflected** at **Boundaries**

When a <u>wave</u> meets a <u>boundary</u> between two materials (a <u>material interface</u>), <u>three</u> things can happen:

1) The wave is <u>absorbed</u> by the second material — the wave <u>transfers energy</u> to the material's energy stores. Often, the energy is transferred to a <u>thermal</u> energy store, which leads to <u>heating</u> (this is how a <u>microwave</u> works, see page 65).

2) The wave is <u>transmitted</u> through the second material — the wave <u>carries on</u> <u>travelling</u> through the new material. This often leads to <u>refraction</u> (see below). Refraction is used in the lenses of <u>glasses</u> and <u>cameras</u>.

3) The wave is <u>reflected</u> — this is where the incoming ray is neither <u>absorbed</u> nor <u>transmitted</u>, but instead is '<u>sent back</u>' away from the second material. This is how <u>echoes</u> are created.

What actually happens depends on the <u>wavelength</u> of the wave and the <u>properties</u> of the <u>materials</u> involved.

Refraction — Waves **Changing Direction** at a **Boundary**

1) Waves travel at <u>different speeds</u> in materials with <u>different densities</u>. So when a wave crosses a <u>boundary</u> between materials it <u>changes speed</u>.

You might see refraction of light talked about in terms of 'optical density'.

2) If a wave hits a boundary at an <u>angle</u>, the change of <u>speed</u> causes a <u>change in direction</u> — <u>refraction</u>.

3) If the wave is travelling <u>along the normal</u> (see below) it will <u>change speed</u>, but it's <u>not refracted</u>.

4) The <u>greater</u> the <u>change</u> in speed, the <u>more</u> a wave <u>bends</u> (changes direction).

5) The wave bends <u>towards the normal</u> if it <u>slows down</u>, and <u>away</u> from the normal if it <u>speeds up</u>.

6) <u>Electromagnetic</u> (EM) waves (see p.63) like light usually travel more <u>slowly</u> in <u>denser</u> materials.

7) How <u>much</u> an <u>EM wave</u> refracts can be affected by its <u>wavelength</u>. <u>Shorter</u> wavelengths <u>bend more</u>. This can lead to the <u>wavelengths spreading out</u> (<u>dispersion</u>), e.g. <u>white</u> light becoming a <u>spectrum</u>.

8) The <u>frequency</u> of a wave <u>stays the same</u> when it crosses a boundary. As $\underline{v = f \times \lambda}$, this means that the <u>change in speed</u> is caused by a <u>change in wavelength</u> — the wavelength <u>decreases</u> if the wave <u>slows down</u>, and <u>increases</u> if it <u>speeds up</u>.

9) You can show <u>refraction</u> using <u>wavefront diagrams</u>. When one part of the wavefront <u>crosses</u> a boundary into a <u>denser</u> material, that part travels <u>slower</u> than the rest of the wavefront, so the wave <u>bends</u>.

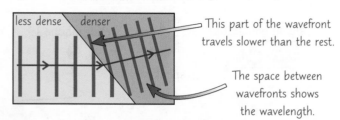

less dense | denser

This part of the wavefront travels slower than the rest.

The space between wavefronts shows the wavelength.

The **Normal** is an **Imaginary Line**

<u>Ray diagrams</u> can be used to show the <u>path</u> that a <u>wave travels</u>. Rays are <u>straight lines</u> that are <u>perpendicular</u> to <u>wavefronts</u>. You need to understand the <u>following terms</u> for ray diagrams:

1) The <u>normal</u> is an <u>imaginary line</u> that's <u>perpendicular</u> (at right angles) to the boundary, at the point where the incoming wave <u>hits</u> the boundary.

2) <u>The angle of incidence</u> is the angle between the <u>incoming</u> (incident) <u>ray</u> and the <u>normal</u>.

3) <u>The angle of refraction</u> is the angle between the <u>refracted ray</u> and the normal.

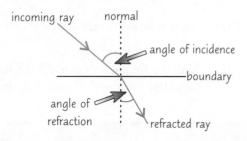

incoming ray | normal

angle of incidence

boundary

angle of refraction

refracted ray

Investigating Refraction

It's time to whip out your ray box and get some <u>refraction</u> going on.

You Need to Do This **Experiment** in a **Dim Room**

1) This experiment uses a <u>ray of light</u>, so it's best to do it in a <u>dim room</u> so you can <u>clearly</u> see the ray.

2) The ray of light must be thin, so you can easily see the <u>middle</u> of the ray when <u>tracing</u> it and <u>measuring angles</u> from it.

3) To do this, you can use a <u>ray box</u> — an enclosed box that contains a <u>light bulb</u>. A <u>thin slit</u> is cut into one of the sides — allowing a <u>thin ray of light</u> out of the box that you can use for your experiment.

You Can Use a **Glass Block** to Investigate **Refraction**

Light is refracted at the <u>boundary</u> between <u>air</u> and <u>glass</u>. You can investigate this by looking at how much light is <u>refracted</u> when it passes through a glass block.

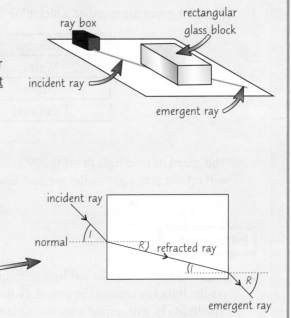

1) Place a <u>rectangular glass block</u> on a piece of <u>paper</u> and <u>trace around it</u>. Use a <u>ray box</u> to shine a ray of light at the <u>middle</u> of one side of the block.

2) <u>Trace</u> the <u>incident ray</u> and the <u>emergent ray</u> on the other side of the block. Remove the block and, with a <u>straight line</u>, <u>join up</u> the <u>incident ray</u> and the emergent ray to show the path of the <u>refracted ray</u> through the block.

3) Draw the <u>normal</u> at the <u>point</u> where the light ray <u>entered</u> the block. Use a protractor to measure the <u>angle</u> between the <u>incident</u> ray and the <u>normal</u> (the <u>angle of incidence</u>, *I*) and the angle between the <u>refracted</u> ray and the <u>normal</u> (the <u>angle of refraction</u>, *R*).

4) Do the <u>same</u> for the point where the ray <u>emerges</u> from the block.

5) You should end up with a <u>diagram</u> that looks like <u>this</u>.

6) <u>Repeat</u> this three times, keeping the angle of incidence as the ray <u>enters</u> the block <u>the same</u>. Calculate an <u>average</u> for each of the angles.

Here's what you should find:

- You should see that the ray of light <u>bends towards</u> the normal as it <u>enters</u> the block (so the <u>angle of refraction</u> is <u>less than</u> the angle of incidence). This is because <u>air</u> has a <u>lower optical density</u> than <u>glass</u>, so the light ray will always <u>slow down</u> when it enters the block.

- You should then see the ray of light bends <u>away from the normal</u> as it <u>leaves</u> the block. This is because the light ray <u>speeds up</u> as it leaves the block and travels through the air.

- It's important to remember that <u>all electromagnetic waves</u> can be refracted — this experiment uses <u>visible light</u> so that you can actually <u>see</u> the ray being <u>refracted</u> as it travels through the block.

Ray boxes produce a thin beam of light...

A thin, bright beam of light will be much <u>easier</u> to trace than a thicker, dimmer one. Not only will you be able to see the light <u>more clearly</u>, but your measurements will be <u>more accurate</u> too.

Warm-Up & Exam Questions

Well they were some refraction-heavy pages. Here are a few questions to check it all went in.

Warm-Up Questions

1) List the three things that can happen when a wave meets a boundary.

2) True or false? The shorter the wavelength of EM radiation, the less the wave is refracted at a boundary.

3) A wave's speed increases as it crosses the boundary between two materials. Assuming the wave hits the boundary at an angle to the normal, will the wave bend towards or away from the normal as it refracts?

4) Name a piece of equipment that can be used to produce a thin beam of light for use in refraction experiments.

Exam Questions

1   **Figure 1** gives the speed at which blue light travels through three different transparent materials.

Material	Speed of blue light (km/s)
Water	225 000
Glass	200 000
Diamond	125 000

Figure 1

The speed of blue light in air is 299 700 km/s. State and explain which of the materials in **Figure 1** will refract blue light by the greatest amount when blue light passes into it at an angle to the normal.

[2 marks]

PRACTICAL

2   **Figure 2** shows a ray of red light entering a glass prism.
As the light ray crosses the boundary between the air and the glass, it refracts.
The light ray will refract a second time as it leaves the glass prism on the other side.

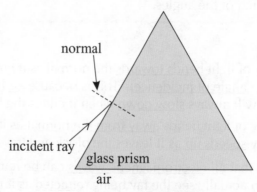

Figure 2

Describe an experiment that could be carried out to measure the angle of incidence, I, and the angle of refraction, R, at both boundaries.

[4 marks]

Electromagnetic Waves

There are lots of different types of <u>electromagnetic wave</u>. Well, <u>seven</u> to be exact...

There's a **Continuous Spectrum** of **EM Waves**

1) <u>Electromagnetic</u> (<u>EM</u>) <u>waves</u> are <u>transverse</u> waves (p.56).

2) They all travel at the <u>same speed</u> through <u>a vacuum</u> (space). But they travel at <u>different speeds</u> in <u>different materials</u> (which can lead to <u>refraction</u> and <u>dispersion</u>, p.60).

Electromagnetic waves aren't vibrations of particles, they're vibrations of electric and magnetic (p.113) fields. This means they can travel through a vacuum.

3) EM waves vary in <u>wavelength</u> from around $\underline{10^{-15} \text{ m}}$ to more than $\underline{10^4 \text{m}}$.

4) We <u>group</u> them based on their <u>wavelength</u> and <u>frequency</u> — there are <u>seven basic types</u>, but the different groups <u>merge</u> to form a <u>continuous spectrum</u>.

RADIO WAVES	MICRO WAVES	INFRA RED	VISIBLE LIGHT	ULTRA VIOLET	X-RAYS	GAMMA RAYS
$1 \text{ m} - 10^4 \text{ m}$	10^{-2} m	10^{-5} m	10^{-7} m	10^{-8} m	10^{-10} m	10^{-15} m

Wavelength

INCREASING FREQUENCY AND DECREASING WAVELENGTH

5) EM waves are <u>generated</u> by a <u>variety</u> of changes in <u>atoms</u> and their <u>nuclei</u>, giving a large <u>range of frequencies</u>. E.g. changes in the <u>nucleus</u> of an atom create <u>gamma rays</u> (p.76) and <u>visible light</u> is often produced by changes in an <u>electron's energy level</u> (p.73). This also explains why atoms can <u>absorb</u> a range of frequencies — each one causes a <u>different change</u>.

6) Our <u>eyes</u> can only detect a <u>small part</u> of this spectrum — <u>visible light</u>. <u>Different colours</u> of light have different <u>wavelengths</u> — from <u>longest</u> to <u>shortest</u>: red, orange, yellow, green, blue, indigo, violet.

7) <u>All</u> EM waves <u>transfer energy</u> from a <u>source</u> to an <u>absorber</u>. For example, when you warm yourself by an <u>electric heater</u>, <u>infrared</u> waves <u>transfer energy</u> from the <u>thermal energy store</u> of the <u>heater</u> (the source) to your <u>thermal energy store</u> (the absorber).

8) The <u>higher the frequency</u> of the EM wave, the <u>more energy</u> it transfers (and so the <u>more dangerous</u> it may be to humans — see p.68).

EM waves are sometimes called EM radiation.

You need to remember all seven types of EM waves...

You need to know the <u>order</u> of the EM waves too. A <u>mnemonic</u> can make this a whole lot easier. My favourite's 'Raging Martians Invaded Venus Using X-ray Guns'. You can make up your own.

Uses of EM Waves

This page is all about how radio waves are generated and what they can be used for.

Radio Waves are Made by Oscillating Charges

1) EM waves are made up of oscillating electric and magnetic fields.

2) Alternating currents (a.c.) (p.108) are made up of oscillating charges. As the charges oscillate, they produce oscillating electric and magnetic fields, i.e. electromagnetic waves.

3) The frequency of the waves produced will be equal to the frequency of the alternating current.

4) You can produce radio waves using an alternating current in an electrical circuit. The object in which charges (electrons) oscillate to create the radio waves is called a transmitter.

5) When transmitted radio waves reach a receiver, the radio waves are absorbed.

6) The energy transferred by the waves is transferred to the electrons in the material of the receiver.

7) This energy causes the electrons to oscillate and, if the receiver is part of a complete electrical circuit, it generates an alternating current.

8) This current has the same frequency as the radio waves that generated it.

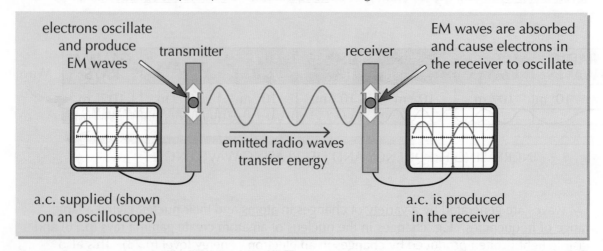

Radio Waves are Used for Communication and Broadcasting

1) Long-wave radio signals (wavelengths of 1 – 10 km) can be received halfway round the world from where they started, because long wavelengths bend around the curved surface of the Earth. This makes it possible for radio signals to be received even if the receiver isn't in the line of sight of the transmitter.

2) Short-wave radio signals (wavelengths of about 10 m – 100 m) can, like long-wave, be received at long distances from the transmitter. That's because they are reflected by the Earth's atmosphere.

3) Bluetooth® uses short-wave radio waves to send data over short distances between devices without wires (e.g. wireless headsets so you can use your phone while driving a car).

4) The radio waves used for TV and FM radio transmissions have very short wavelengths. To get reception, you must be in direct sight of the transmitter — the signal doesn't bend or travel far through buildings.

Uses of EM Waves

Believe it or not, <u>microwaves</u> are used in <u>microwave ovens</u>. For more uses of microwaves, read on.

Microwaves and Radio Waves are Used by Satellites

1) Communication to and from <u>satellites</u> (including satellite TV signals and satellite phones) uses EM waves which can <u>pass easily</u> through the Earth's <u>watery atmosphere</u>.

2) These waves are <u>usually microwaves</u>, but can sometimes be relatively high frequency <u>radio waves</u>.

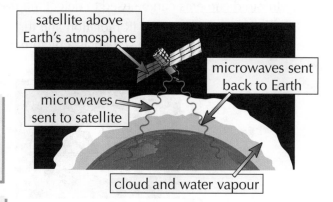

satellite above Earth's atmosphere

microwaves sent back to Earth

microwaves sent to satellite

cloud and water vapour

3) For satellite TV, the signal from a <u>transmitter</u> is transmitted into space and picked up by the satellite receiver dish <u>orbiting</u> thousands of kilometres above the Earth.

4) The satellite <u>transmits</u> the signal back to Earth in a different direction, where it's received by a <u>satellite dish</u> on the ground.

Microwave Ovens Use a Different Wavelength from Satellites

1) In <u>communications</u>, the microwaves used need to <u>pass through</u> the Earth's watery atmosphere.

2) In <u>microwave ovens</u>, the microwaves need to be <u>absorbed</u> by <u>water molecules</u> in food — so they use a <u>different</u> wavelength to those used in satellite communications.

3) The microwaves penetrate up to a few centimetres into the food before being <u>absorbed</u> and <u>transferring</u> the energy they are carrying to the <u>water molecules</u> in the food, causing the water to <u>heat up</u>.

4) The water molecules then <u>transfer</u> this energy to the rest of the molecules in the food <u>by heating</u> — which <u>quickly cooks</u> the food.

Some microwaves pass through water, others are absorbed by water...

The <u>wavelength</u> of an EM wave affects whether it is absorbed, transmitted or reflected by a substance (p.60). The microwaves used in a microwave oven are <u>absorbed</u> by water. The microwaves used in satellite communications have a <u>different wavelength</u> that <u>won't</u> be absorbed by water in the atmosphere.

Uses of EM Waves

Infrared radiation is another ridiculously useful EM wave. You can use it to cook your dinner, catch criminals in the dark, and change the TV channel without getting up from your favourite chair.

Infrared Radiation Can be Used to Monitor Temperature...

1) Infrared (IR) radiation is given out by all hot objects — the hotter the object, the more IR radiation it gives out.

2) Infrared cameras can be used to detect infrared radiation and monitor temperature.

3) The camera detects the IR radiation and turns it into an electrical signal, which is displayed on a screen as a picture. This is called thermal imaging.

Different colours represent different amounts of IR radiation being detected. Here, the redder the colour, the more infrared radiation is being detected.

4) Thermal imaging is used by police to see suspects that are trying to escape or hide in the dark.

5) Infrared sensors can be used in security systems. If a change in infrared radiation is detected, an alarm sounds or a security light turns on.

...Or Increase it

1) Absorbing IR radiation causes objects to get hotter. Food can be cooked using IR radiation — the temperature of the food increases when it absorbs IR radiation, e.g. from a toaster's heating element.

2) Electric heaters heat a room in the same way. Electric heaters contain a long piece of wire that heats up when a current flows through it. This wire then emits lots of infrared radiation (and a little visible light — the wire glows). The emitted IR radiation is absorbed by objects and the air in the room — energy is transferred by the IR waves to the thermal energy stores of the objects, causing their temperature to increase.

Infrared Can Also Transfer Information

Infrared radiation can also be used to transfer information.

1) For example, it can be used to send files between mobile phones or laptops. The distances must be fairly small and the receiver must be in the line of sight of the emitter.

2) This is also how TV remote controls work. In fact, some mobile phones now have built in software which means that you can use your phone as a TV remote.

3) Optical fibres are thin glass or plastic fibres that can carry data (e.g. from telephones or computers) over long distances as pulses of infrared radiation. They usually use a single wavelength to prevent dispersion (p.60), which can otherwise cause some information to be lost.

Uses of EM Waves

And we're still not finished with <u>uses</u> of EM <u>waves</u> — there's just no end to their talents...

Photography Uses Visible Light

1) <u>Visible light</u> is the light that we can <u>see</u>. We use it for <u>illuminating</u> things so that we can see them.
2) <u>Photographic film</u> reacts to light to form an image. This is how traditional <u>cameras</u> create <u>photographs</u>.
3) <u>Digital cameras</u> contain <u>image sensors</u>, which detect <u>visible light</u> and generate an electrical signal. This signal is then <u>converted</u> into an image that can be stored digitally or <u>printed</u>.

Ultraviolet is Used in Fluorescent Lamps

1) <u>Fluorescence</u> is a property of certain chemicals, where <u>ultraviolet</u> (<u>UV</u>) radiation is <u>absorbed</u> and then <u>visible light</u> is <u>emitted</u>. That's why fluorescent colours look so <u>bright</u> — they actually <u>emit light</u>.
2) <u>Fluorescent lights</u> use UV to <u>emit</u> visible light. They're <u>energy-efficient</u> (p.46) so they're good to use when light is needed for <u>long periods</u> (like in your <u>classroom</u>).
3) <u>Security pens</u> can be used to <u>mark</u> property (e.g. laptops). Under <u>UV light</u> the ink will <u>glow</u>, but it's <u>invisible</u> otherwise, helping to <u>identify</u> stolen property.
4) <u>Bank notes</u> and <u>passports</u> use a similar technique to detect <u>forgeries</u> — genuine notes and passports have <u>special markings</u> that only show up under UV light.
5) Ultraviolet radiation is sometimes used to <u>sterilise water</u>. It <u>kills bacteria</u> in the water, making it <u>safe</u> to drink. (Gamma rays are used in a similar way, see below.)

X-rays Let Us See Inside Things

1) <u>X-rays</u> can be used to view the <u>internal structure</u> of <u>objects</u> and <u>materials</u>, including our <u>bodies</u>.
2) They affect <u>photographic</u> film in the same way as <u>light</u>, meaning you can take <u>X-ray photographs</u>. But X-ray images are usually formed <u>electronically</u> these days.
3) <u>Radiographers</u> in <u>hospitals</u> take <u>X-ray images</u> to help doctors diagnose <u>broken bones</u> — X-rays are <u>transmitted by flesh</u> but are <u>absorbed</u> by <u>denser material</u> like <u>bones</u> or metal.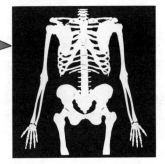
4) To produce an <u>X-ray image</u>, X-ray radiation is directed <u>through the object</u> or <u>body</u> onto a <u>detector</u>. The <u>brighter bits</u> of the image are where <u>fewer X-rays</u> get through, producing a <u>negative image</u> (the plate starts off <u>all white</u>).
5) X-rays are also used in <u>airport security scanners</u> to detect hidden objects that can't be detected with <u>metal detectors</u>.

Gamma Rays are Used for Sterilising Things

1) <u>Gamma rays</u> are used to <u>sterilise</u> medical instruments — they <u>kill</u> microbes (e.g. bacteria).
2) <u>Food</u> can be <u>sterilised</u> in the same way — again by <u>killing microbes</u>. This keeps the food <u>fresh for longer</u>, without having to freeze it, cook it or preserve it some other way, and it's <u>perfectly safe</u> to eat.
3) Some <u>medical imaging</u> techniques use gamma rays to <u>detect cancer</u>.
4) Gamma radiation is used in <u>cancer treatment</u>, radiation is targeted at cancer cells to <u>kill them</u>. Doctors have to be careful to <u>minimise</u> the damage to <u>healthy cells</u> when treating cancer like this.

Dangers of EM Waves

Okay, so you know how <u>useful</u> electromagnetic radiation can be — well, it can also be pretty <u>dangerous</u>.

EM Radiation Can be Harmful to People

1) As you saw on p.60, when EM waves meet a <u>boundary</u> they can be <u>absorbed</u>, <u>transmitted</u>, <u>refracted</u> or <u>reflected</u>.

2) What happens depends on the materials at the <u>boundary</u> and the <u>wavelength</u> of the EM wave. E.g. some materials <u>absorb</u> some wavelengths of <u>light</u> but <u>reflect</u> others. This is what causes things to be a certain <u>colour</u>.

3) Differences in how EM waves are transmitted, reflected and absorbed have implications for <u>human health</u>.

> In general, the <u>higher the frequency</u> of the EM wave, the <u>more energy</u> it transfers and so the <u>more potentially dangerous</u> it is for humans.

Different EM Waves Have Different Effects on the Body

1) <u>Radio waves</u> are transmitted through the body <u>without</u> being <u>absorbed</u>.

2) Some wavelengths of <u>microwaves</u> can be <u>absorbed</u>, causing <u>heating</u> of cells, which may be dangerous.

3) <u>Infrared</u> (<u>IR</u>) and <u>visible light</u> are mostly <u>reflected</u> or <u>absorbed</u> by the skin, causing some <u>heating</u> too. IR can cause <u>burns</u> if the skin gets <u>too hot</u>.

4) <u>Ultraviolet</u> (<u>UV</u>) is also <u>absorbed</u> by the skin. But it has a <u>higher frequency</u>, so it is potentially <u>more dangerous</u>. It's a type of <u>ionising radiation</u> (p.76) and when absorbed it can cause <u>damage</u> to cells on the <u>surface of your skin</u>, which could lead to <u>skin cancer</u>. It can also damage your <u>eyes</u> and cause a variety of <u>eye conditions</u> or even <u>blindness</u>.

Most of the UV radiation produced by the Sun that hits the Earth's atmosphere gets absorbed.

5) <u>X-rays</u> and <u>gamma rays</u> are also <u>ionising</u>, so they can cause mutations and damage cells too (which can lead to cancer). But they have <u>even higher frequencies</u>, so transfer even <u>more energy</u>, causing even <u>more damage</u>. They can also pass through the skin and be absorbed by <u>deeper tissues</u>.

The risks and benefits must be weighed up...

<u>Ionising radiation</u> can be <u>dangerous</u>, but the risk can be worth taking. <u>X-ray machines</u> used to be installed in shoe shops for use in <u>shoe fittings</u>. They were removed when people realised X-rays were harmful and the <u>risks far outweighed</u> the <u>benefits</u> of using X-rays rather than tape measures...

Warm-Up & Exam Questions

EM radiation — so many uses, so many risks. Test your memory by answering these questions.

Warm-Up Questions

1) Are EM waves transverse or longitudinal?
2) True or false? The speed at which an EM wave travels in a vacuum depends on its wavelength.
3) Which type of EM wave has the highest frequency?
4) True or false? Changes in atoms can generate EM waves.
5) State one possible use of radio waves.
6) Explain how microwave ovens heat food.
7) What type of radiation is used in optical fibres?
8) Give one use of gamma radiation.
9) True or false? The higher the frequency of EM radiation, the more potentially dangerous it is for humans.

Exam Questions

1   **Figure 1** shows an image of the bones in a patient's foot.

   (a)   Name a type of EM radiation that could have been used to produce this photograph.

   [1 mark]

   (b)   State **one** risk to the patient from being exposed to this type of radiation.

   [1 mark]

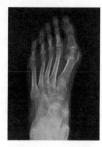

Figure 1

2   An alternating current is passed through a transmitter in order to produce radio waves with a wavelength of 8 km. The radio waves reach a receiver which is connected to a complete electrical circuit.

   (a)   Describe the effect of the incoming wave on the receiver and its circuit.

   [3 marks]

   The receiver is located in a built-up area. A resident is concerned that being exposed to radio waves may cause health problems.

   (b)   Explain whether the resident is right to be concerned.

   [1 mark]

3   A patient is suffering with a skin condition called psoriasis. She is offered UVB phototherapy to treat the condition, where she will be exposed to ultraviolet radiation three times a week.

   Describe the possible dangers involved with this treatment and any precautions that may be taken to minimise the risk of the patient being harmed by this treatment.

   [4 marks]

Revision Summary for Section 3

Wave goodbye to Section 3 — you've finally reached the end. Time to see how much you've learnt.
- Try these questions and tick off each one when you get it right.
- When you've done all the questions under a heading and are completely happy with it, tick it off.

Wave Properties (p.55-58) ☑

1) What is the amplitude, wavelength and frequency of a wave? ☑

2) True or false? The period of a wave is the number of complete cycles of the wave that passes a point per second. ☑

3) Describe the difference between transverse and longitudinal waves and give an example of each. ☑

4) State the equation that relates wave speed, distance and time. ☑

5) Describe an experiment you could do to measure the speed of ripples in water. ☑

Refraction (p.60-61) ☑

6) Explain, in terms of wave speed, what is meant by refraction. ☑

7) True or false? A wave travelling along the normal to a boundary will not be refracted as it crosses the boundary. ☑

8) State why experiments investigating the refraction of light should be conducted in a dim room. ☑

Uses and Dangers of Electromagnetic Waves (p.63-68) ☑

9) True or false? All electromagnetic waves are transverse. ☑

10) Name two types of EM wave that have a higher frequency than ultraviolet radiation. ☑

11) Name all of the types of EM wave in order of shortest wavelength to longest. ☑

12) True or false? The human eye can detect all types of EM wave. ☑

13) What kind of current is used to generate radio waves in an antenna? ☑

14) What type of radiation is used in thermal imaging cameras? ☑

15) Give two uses of ultraviolet radiation. ☑

16) Give a non-medical use of X-rays. ☑

17) Which is potentially more dangerous, an EM wave with a high or a low frequency? ☑

18) Give one potential danger of X-rays and gamma rays. ☑

Developing the Model of the Atom

We used to think <u>atoms</u> were tiny solid spheres (like ball bearings), but they're <u>much more complex</u> than that.

The Theory of **Atomic Structure** Has **Changed** Over Time

1) In 1897 <u>J. J. Thomson</u> discovered that <u>electrons</u> could be <u>removed</u> from atoms, so atoms must be made up of smaller bits. He suggested the <u>'plum-pudding' model</u> — that atoms were <u>spheres of positive charge</u> with tiny negative electrons <u>stuck in them</u> like fruit in a plum pudding.

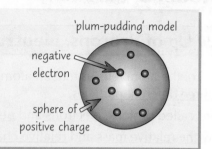
'plum-pudding' model
negative electron
sphere of positive charge

2) That "plum pudding" theory didn't last very long though. In 1909, <u>Rutherford</u> and <u>Marsden</u> tried firing a beam of <u>alpha particles</u> (see p.76) at <u>thin gold foil</u>. From the plum-pudding model, they expected the particles to <u>pass straight through</u> the gold sheet, or only be <u>slightly deflected</u>.

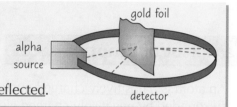
gold foil
alpha source
detector

3) But although most of the particles did go <u>straight through</u> the sheet, some were deflected more than they had expected, and a few were <u>deflected back</u> the way they had come — something the plum-pudding model <u>couldn't explain</u>.

4) Rutherford realised this meant that <u>most of the mass</u> of the atom was concentrated at the <u>centre</u> in a <u>tiny nucleus</u>.

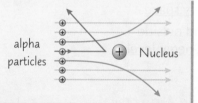
alpha particles
Nucleus

5) He also realised that most of an atom is just <u>empty space</u>, and that the nucleus must have a <u>positive charge</u>, since it repelled the positive alpha particles.

6) This led to the creation of the <u>nuclear model</u> of the atom (see next page).

7) <u>Niels Bohr</u> tweaked Rutherford's idea a few years later by proposing a model where the electrons were in <u>fixed orbits</u> at <u>set distances</u> from the nucleus. These fixed orbits were called <u>energy levels</u> (p.73).

8) He suggested that electrons can <u>only</u> exist in these fixed orbits (or <u>shells</u>), and not anywhere in between.

9) This is known as the <u>Bohr model</u> and is <u>pretty close</u> to our currently accepted model of the atom.

WORKING SCIENTIFICALLY

Rutherford's experiment helped adapt the model of the atom...

Rutherford and his lab of scientists made a <u>hypothesis</u>, did an <u>investigation</u> and then <u>analysed</u> the data they got from it. By doing this, they showed that the plum pudding model of the atom must be wrong, so it was <u>changed</u>. This is a great example of the <u>scientific method</u> (see page 2) in action.

Current Model of the Atom

Due to lots of scientists doing lots of <u>experiments</u>, we now have a better idea of what the atom's really like. We now know about the particles in atoms — <u>protons</u>, <u>neutrons</u> and <u>electrons</u>.

The **Current Model** of the Atom

Atoms are Made Up **of Protons, Neutrons** and **Electrons**...

1) The <u>current model</u> of the atom tells us that all atoms are made out of <u>three different particles</u>.

2) These particles are called <u>protons</u>, <u>electrons</u> and <u>neutrons</u>.

3) You need to know the <u>relative mass</u> and <u>relative charge</u> of each of these particles.

Particle	Relative Mass	Relative Charge
Proton	1	+1
Neutron	1	0
Electron	0.0005	−1

... and a lot of **Empty Space**

1) An atom is a <u>positively charged nucleus</u> surrounded by <u>negatively charged electrons</u>.

2) Virtually all the <u>mass</u> of the atom is in the <u>nucleus</u>. The nucleus is <u>tiny</u> — about <u>10 000</u> times <u>smaller</u> than the whole atom. It contains <u>protons</u> (which are <u>positively charged</u>) and <u>neutrons</u> (which are <u>neutral</u>). The rest of the atom is mostly <u>empty space</u>.

3) The <u>negative electrons</u> whizz round outside the nucleus in <u>fixed orbits</u> called <u>energy levels</u> or <u>shells</u>. They give the atom its <u>overall size</u> of around $\underline{1 \times 10^{-10}}$ m.

4) Atoms are <u>neutral</u>, so <u>the number of protons = the number of electrons</u>. This is because <u>protons</u> and <u>electrons</u> have an <u>equal</u> but <u>opposite charge</u>.

5) If an atom <u>loses an electron</u> it becomes a <u>positive ion</u>. If it <u>gains</u> an electron it becomes a <u>negative ion</u> (p.73).

6) Atoms can <u>join together</u> to form <u>molecules</u> — e.g. molecules of <u>oxygen</u> gas are made up of two oxygen atoms bonded together. <u>Small molecules</u> like this have a typical size of $\underline{1 \times 10^{-10}}$ m — the <u>same sort of scale</u> as an atom.

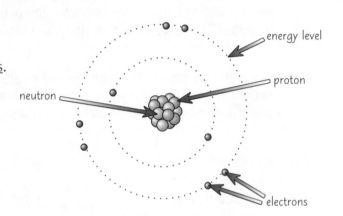

Lots of Atomic Quantities use **Standard Form**

The quantities to do with atoms are <u>really tiny</u>, so they're written in <u>standard form</u>:

A is a number between 1 and 10.

$$A \times 10^n$$

n is the number of places the decimal point would move if you wrote the number out in decimal form.

If n is positive you know you're dealing with a large number. If n is negative you're dealing with a small number.

You'll find standard form all over the place...

Physics covers everything from tiny particles to giant stars. That means dealing with some <u>really big numbers</u> and some <u>really small numbers</u>. So, unless you want to spend all day writing zeros you've got to get used to <u>standard form</u>. 1×10^{-10} m is a lot easier than writing 0.0000000001 m.

Electron Energy Levels

There's some <u>quirky</u> stuff on this page — and the best part is that you can tell everyone you've been doing a little <u>quantum physics</u> today. Honestly. And if you study physics to a higher level, things get even <u>quirkier</u>.

Electrons can be Excited to Higher Energy Levels

1) <u>Electrons</u> in an atom sit in <u>different energy levels</u> or shells.

2) Each <u>energy level</u> is a different distance from the <u>nucleus</u>.

3) An inner electron can <u>move up</u> to a higher energy level if it <u>absorbs electromagnetic (EM) radiation</u> with the right amount of <u>energy</u>.

4) When it does move up, it moves to an <u>empty</u> or <u>partially filled shell</u> and is said to be 'excited'.

5) The electron will then quickly <u>fall back</u> to its <u>original energy level</u>, and in doing so will <u>emit</u> (lose) the <u>same amount</u> of energy it <u>absorbed</u>.

6) The energy is <u>carried away</u> by <u>EM radiation</u>.

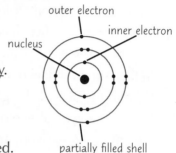

EM radiation in

The electron absorbs the energy carried by the EM radiation and is excited to the next (higher) energy level.

EM radiation out

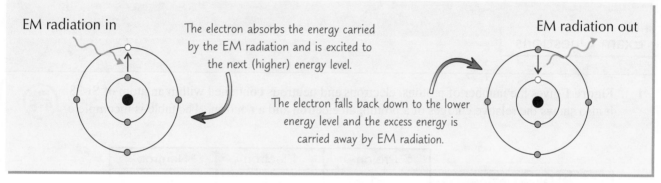

The electron falls back down to the lower energy level and the excess energy is carried away by EM radiation.

7) The part of the <u>EM spectrum</u> the radiation <u>emitted from the atom</u> is from depends on its <u>energy</u>. This depends on <u>the energy levels</u> the electron moves between. A <u>higher energy</u> means a <u>higher frequency</u> of EM radiation — p.63.

- As you move <u>further out</u> from the nucleus, the energy levels get <u>closer together</u> (so the <u>difference in energy</u> between two levels <u>next to</u> each other gets <u>smaller</u>).

- This means that an <u>excited</u> electron <u>falling</u> from the <u>third</u> energy level to the <u>second</u> would release <u>less energy</u> than an excited electron falling from the <u>second</u> energy level to the <u>first</u>. So the <u>frequency</u> of the generated radiation <u>decreases</u> as you get <u>further</u> from the <u>nucleus</u>.

8) Often, <u>visible light</u> is released when electrons move between energy levels.

9) Changes <u>within the nucleus itself</u> lead to the production of high energy, high frequency <u>gamma rays</u> (p.76).

An Atom is Ionised if it Loses an Electron

1) If an <u>outer electron</u> absorbs radiation with <u>enough energy</u>, it can move <u>so far</u> that it <u>leaves the atom</u>.

2) It is now a <u>free electron</u> and the atom is said to have been <u>ionised</u>.

3) The atom is now a <u>positive ion</u>. It's <u>positive</u> because there are now <u>more protons</u> than <u>electrons</u>.

4) An atom can lose <u>more than one electron</u>. The <u>more</u> electrons it loses, the <u>greater</u> its positive charge.

Warm-Up & Exam Questions

Atoms may be tiny, but you could bag some big marks in your exams if you know them inside out.
Here are some questions to check just how great your understanding of atoms really is...

Warm-Up Questions

1) Describe Thompson's 'plum pudding' model of the atom.
2) What are the relative masses of protons, neutrons and electrons?
3) True or false? Most of an atom's volume is made up of empty space.
4) In the current model of the atom, where are the protons located?
5) What is the overall charge of an atom?
6) What is the typical size of an atom?
7) True or false? An atom must gain an electron in order to become a positively charged ion.

Exam Questions

1   **Figure 1** gives the number of protons, electrons and neutrons contained within an atom of Si-28.
    It also shows the relative charges of a proton, an electron and a neutron. The table is incomplete.

	Proton	Electron	Neutron
Relative Charge	+1	-1	
Number Present in Si-28	14		14

Figure 1

(a)   Complete **Figure 1**.

[2 marks]

(b)   Describe how electrons are arranged in the Bohr model of the atom.

[2 marks]

An electron in Si-28 absorbs 6.9×10^{-19} J of energy and as a result is excited to a higher energy level.
After some time the electron returns to its original energy level by emitting electromagnetic radiation.

(c)   State how much energy is emitted by the electron as it returns to its original energy level.

[1 mark]

Now the electron absorbs enough energy to be completely removed from the atom.

(d)   State the relative charge of the silicon ion that is formed as a result.

[1 mark]

2   Rutherford investigated the structure of the atom by firing a beam of alpha particles at gold foil.
    Describe the results that Rutherford observed and the conclusions they led him to.

[4 marks]

Isotopes

Isotopes of an element look pretty similar, but watch out — they have <u>different numbers of neutrons</u>.

Atoms of the Same Element have the Same Number of Protons

1) All atoms of each <u>element</u> have a <u>set number</u> of <u>protons</u> (so each nucleus has a given <u>positive charge</u>).

2) The <u>number</u> of protons in an atom is its <u>atomic number</u> or its <u>proton number</u>.

3) The <u>mass (nucleon) number</u> of an atom (the <u>mass</u> of the <u>nucleus</u>)
   is the <u>number of protons</u> + the <u>number of neutrons</u> in its nucleus.

> Example: An oxygen atom has the chemical symbol $^{16}_{8}O$.
>
> Mass number ⟶ 16
> 8 O ⟵ Element symbol (oxygen)
> Atomic number ⟶
>
> • Oxygen has an <u>atomic number</u> of 8. All oxygen atoms have <u>8 protons</u>.
> • This atom of oxygen has a <u>mass number</u> of 16.
>   Since it has 8 protons, it must have 16 − 8 = <u>8 neutrons</u>.

Isotopes are Different Forms of the Same Element

1) <u>Isotopes</u> of an element are atoms with the <u>same</u> number of <u>protons</u> (the same <u>atomic number</u>) but a different number of <u>neutrons</u> (a different <u>mass number</u>).

2) <u>Isotopes</u> can be written as, e.g., <u>oxygen-18</u>. This means that the <u>mass</u> number is <u>18</u>.

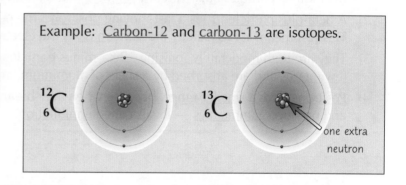

Example: <u>Carbon-12</u> and <u>carbon-13</u> are isotopes.

$^{12}_{6}C$ $^{13}_{6}C$

one extra neutron

3) <u>All</u> elements have different isotopes, but there are usually only one or two <u>stable</u> ones.

4) The other <u>unstable</u> isotopes tend to <u>decay</u> into <u>other elements</u> and give out <u>radiation</u> as they try to become <u>more stable</u>. This process is called <u>radioactive decay</u>.

5) Radioactive substances <u>spit out</u> one or more types of <u>ionising</u> radiation when they decay: <u>alpha</u>, <u>beta</u> or <u>gamma</u> (see next page). They can also emit <u>neutrons</u> (n).

Isotopes — Same-same, but different...

Isotopes of an element have lots in common — they have the <u>same number</u> of <u>protons</u> and <u>electrons</u>. What's <u>different</u> is their <u>mass numbers</u> — this is because they have different numbers of <u>neutrons</u>.

Ionising Radiation

Alpha, beta and gamma radiation — they all come from the nucleus, but they have some key differences...

Nuclear Radiation Ionises Atoms

1) Ionising radiation is any radiation that can knock electrons from atoms.
2) How likely it is that each type of radiation will ionise an atom varies.

Alpha Particles are Helium Nuclei

1) Alpha radiation is when an alpha particle (α) is emitted from the nucleus. An α-particle is two neutrons and two protons (like a helium nucleus).
2) They don't penetrate very far into materials and are stopped quickly — they can only travel a few cm in air and are absorbed by a thin sheet of paper.
3) Because of their size they are strongly ionising.

Beta Particles can be Electrons or Positrons

1) A beta-minus particle (β^-) is simply a fast-moving electron released by the nucleus. Beta-minus particles have virtually no mass and a relative charge of –1.
2) A beta-plus particle (β^+) is a fast-moving positron. The positron is the antiparticle of the electron. This just means it has exactly the same mass as the electron, but a positive (+1) charge.
3) They are both moderately ionising. Beta-minus particles have a range in air of a few metres and are absorbed by a sheet of aluminium (around 5 mm thick).
4) Positrons have a smaller range, because when they hit an electron the two destroy each other and produce gamma rays — this is called annihilation.

Gamma Rays are EM Waves with a Short Wavelength

1) After a nucleus has decayed, it often undergoes nuclear rearrangement and releases some energy. Gamma rays (γ) are waves of EM radiation (p.63) released by the nucleus that carry away this energy.
2) They penetrate far into materials without being stopped and will travel a long distance through air.
3) This means they are weakly ionising because they tend to pass through rather than collide with atoms. Eventually they hit something and do damage.
4) They can be absorbed by thick sheets of lead or metres of concrete.

Alpha particles are more ionising than beta particles...

... and beta particles are more ionising than gamma rays. Make sure you've got that clearly memorised, as well as what makes up each type of radiation, as this isn't the last you'll see of this stuff. No siree.

Nuclear Equations

Nuclear equations show radioactive decay and once you get the hang of them they're dead easy. Get going.

Mass and Atomic Numbers Have to Balance

1) Nuclear equations are a way of showing radioactive decay by using element symbols (p.75).
2) They're written in the form: atom before decay → atom after decay + radiation emitted.
3) There is one golden rule to remember: the total mass and atomic numbers must be equal on both sides.

Alpha Decay Decreases the Charge and Mass of the Nucleus

When a nucleus emits an alpha particle, it loses two protons and two neutrons, so:

- the mass number decreases by 4.
- the atomic number decreases by 2.

$$^{238}_{92}U \rightarrow {}^{234}_{90}Th + {}^{4}_{2}\alpha$$

| mass number: | 238 | → | 234 | + | 4 | (= 238) |
| atomic number: | 92 | → | 90 | + | 2 | (= 92) |

Beta-minus Decay Increases the Charge of the Nucleus

In a beta-minus decay, a neutron changes into a proton and an electron, so:

- the mass number doesn't change — as it has lost a neutron but gained a proton.
- the atomic number increases by 1 — because it has one more proton.

$$^{14}_{6}C \rightarrow {}^{14}_{7}N + {}^{0}_{-1}\beta$$

| mass number: | 14 | → | 14 | + | 0 | (= 14) |
| atomic number: | 6 | → | 7 | + | (−1) | (= 6) |

Positron Emission Decreases the Charge of the Nucleus

In beta-plus decay, a proton changes into a neutron and a positron, so:

- the mass number doesn't change — as it has lost a proton but gained a neutron.
- the atomic number decreases by 1 — because it has one less proton.

$$^{18}_{9}F \rightarrow {}^{18}_{8}O + {}^{0}_{1}\beta$$

| mass number: | 18 | → | 18 | + | 0 | (= 18) |
| atomic number: | 9 | → | 8 | + | 1 | (= 9) |

Neutron Emission Decreases the Mass of the Nucleus

When a nucleus emits a neutron:

- the mass number decreases by 1 — as it has lost a neutron.
- the atomic number stays the same.

$$^{13}_{4}Be \rightarrow {}^{12}_{4}Be + {}^{1}_{0}n$$

| mass number: | 13 | → | 12 | + | 1 | (= 13) |
| atomic number: | 4 | → | 4 | + | 0 | (= 4) |

Gamma Rays Don't Change the Charge or Mass of the Nucleus

1) Gamma rays (γ) are a way of getting rid of excess energy from an atom.
   The nucleus goes from an excited state to a more stable state by emitting a gamma ray.

2) The mass and atomic numbers stay the same after a gamma ray has been emitted.

Warm-Up & Exam Questions

If you're confident you know your alpha particles from your gamma rays, try the questions below...

Warm-Up Questions

1) An atom of sodium has a mass number of 23 and an atomic number of 11. How many neutrons does it have?
2) True or false? Isotopes of an element have different atomic numbers.
3) What is meant by the term 'ionising radiation'?
4) Which type of ionising radiation has the greatest mass: alpha, beta or gamma?
5) True or false? A 5 mm sheet of aluminium will completely block gamma rays.
6) An atom undergoes a single beta-plus decay. What is the change in its atomic number?
7) An atom of Ar-40 undergoes gamma decay. What is the mass number of the resulting nucleus?

Exam Questions

1   Alpha, beta and gamma radiation sources were used to direct radiation at thin sheets of paper and aluminium. A detector was used to measure where radiation had passed through the sheets. The results are shown in **Figure 1**.

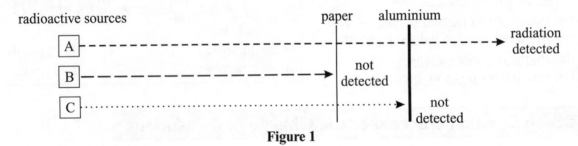

Figure 1

Name the type of radiation that source C emits. Explain your answer.

[2 marks]

2   **Figure 2** contains information about three atoms.

	Mass number	Atomic number
Atom A	32	17
Atom B	33	17
Atom C	32	16

Figure 2

(a)   Define the term 'mass number' in the context of atoms.

[1 mark]

(b)   State and explain which two atoms in **Figure 2** are isotopes of the same element.

[2 marks]

(c)   Radon-219 decays by alpha emission to form an isotope of polonium. **Figure 3** shows an incomplete nuclear equation for this decay.

$$^{219}_{86}\text{Rn} \rightarrow \, ^{215}_{X}\text{Po} + \, ^{4}_{2}\alpha$$

Figure 3

Determine the atomic number, X, of the polonium atom.

[1 mark]

Background Radiation and Activity

Forget love — <u>radiation</u> is <u>all around</u>. Don't panic too much though — it's usually a pretty <u>small amount</u>.

Background Radiation Comes from Many Sources

<u>Background radiation</u> is the <u>low-level</u> radiation that's around us <u>all the time</u>. It comes from:

1) Radioactivity of naturally occurring <u>unstable isotopes</u> which are <u>all around us</u> — in the <u>air</u>, in <u>some foods</u>, in <u>building materials</u> and in some of the <u>rocks</u> under our feet.

Coloured bits indicate more radiation from rocks.

2) Radiation from <u>space</u>, which is known as <u>cosmic rays</u>. These come mostly from the <u>Sun</u>. Luckily, the Earth's <u>atmosphere protects</u> us from much of this radiation.

3) Radiation due to <u>human activity</u>, e.g. <u>fallout</u> from <u>nuclear explosions</u> or radiation from <u>nuclear waste</u>. But this represents a <u>tiny</u> proportion of the total background radiation.

Radioactivity is a Totally Random Process

1) <u>Radioactive sources</u> contain <u>radioactive isotopes</u> that give out <u>radiation</u> from the nuclei of their atoms.

2) This process is entirely <u>random</u>. This means that if you have 1000 unstable nuclei, you can't say when <u>any one of them</u> is going to decay, or which one will decay <u>next</u>.

3) If there are <u>lots</u> of nuclei though, you <u>can</u> predict <u>how many</u> will have decayed in a <u>given time</u> based on the <u>half-life</u> of the source (see next page). The rate at which a source decays is called its <u>activity</u>.

4) Activity is measured in <u>becquerels</u>, <u>Bq</u>. 1 Bq is <u>1 decay per second</u>.

5) Activity can be measured with a <u>Geiger-Müller tube</u>, which <u>clicks</u> each time it detects radiation. The tube can be attached to a <u>counter</u>, which displays the number of clicks per second (the <u>count-rate</u>).

6) You can also detect radiation using <u>photographic film</u>. The <u>more</u> radiation the film's exposed to, the <u>darker</u> it becomes (just like when you expose it to light).

Your exposure to background radiation depends on where you live...

Background radiation comes from many sources, from <u>food and drink</u> to <u>cosmic rays</u>, but mostly it comes from the <u>ground</u> and is given out by certain rocks, like granite. That's why some parts of the UK have higher levels of <u>background radiation</u> than others. Areas like Cornwall and Devon, where there's lots of granite, have higher background radiation levels than is average for the UK. But they do have lovely beaches.

Half-Life and Dangers of Radiation

How quickly <u>unstable nuclei</u> decay is measured using <u>activity</u> and <u>half-life</u> — two very important terms.

The **Radioactivity** of a Source **Decreases Over Time**

1) Each time a radioactive nucleus <u>decays</u>, that radioactive nucleus <u>disappears</u>.
   As the <u>unstable nuclei</u> all steadily disappear, the activity <u>as a whole</u> will <u>decrease</u>.

2) For <u>some</u> isotopes it takes <u>just a few hours</u> before nearly all the
   unstable nuclei have <u>decayed</u>, whilst others last for <u>millions of years</u>.

3) The problem with trying to <u>measure</u> this is that <u>the activity never reaches zero</u>, so
   we have to use the idea of <u>half-life</u> to measure how quickly the activity <u>drops off</u>.

> The <u>half-life</u> is the <u>average</u> time taken for the
> <u>number of radioactive nuclei</u> of an isotope to <u>halve</u>.

Half-life can also be described as the time taken for the activity to halve.

4) A <u>short half-life</u> means the <u>activity falls quickly</u>, because the nuclei are very <u>unstable</u> and <u>rapidly decay</u>.

5) Sources with a short half-life are <u>dangerous</u> because of the <u>high</u> amount
   of radiation they emit at the start, but they <u>quickly</u> become <u>safe</u>.

6) A <u>long half-life</u> means the activity <u>falls more slowly</u> because <u>most</u> of the nuclei don't decay
   <u>for a long time</u> — the source just sits there, releasing <u>small</u> amounts of radiation for a <u>long time</u>.

7) This can be dangerous because <u>nearby areas</u> are <u>exposed</u> to radiation for (<u>millions of</u>) <u>years</u>.

EXAMPLE: **The activity of a radioactive sample is measured as 640 Bq.**
One hour later it has fallen to 160 Bq. Find its half-life.

1) Count how many <u>half-lives</u> it
   took to <u>fall</u> to 160 Bq.

   Initial activity: after 1 half-life: after 2 half-lives:

   640   (÷2) →   320   (÷2) →   160

2) Calculate the <u>half-life of the sample</u>.   One hour is two half-lives — so the half-life is
   1 hour ÷ 2 = 30 min

Finding the **Half-Life** of a Sample using a **Graph**

1) If you plot a graph of <u>activity</u> <u>against</u>
   <u>time</u> (taking into account <u>background</u>
   <u>radiation</u>, see previous page), it will
   <u>always</u> be shaped like this one.

2) The <u>half-life</u> is found from the graph by
   finding the <u>time interval</u> on the <u>bottom</u>
   <u>axis</u> corresponding to a <u>halving</u> of the
   <u>activity</u> on the <u>vertical axis</u>.

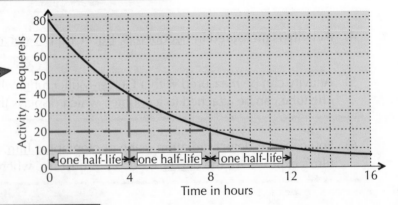

Radiation **Damages** Cells by **Ionisation**

1) Radiation can <u>enter living cells</u> and <u>ionise atoms and molecules</u> within them.
   This can lead to <u>tissue damage</u>.

2) <u>Lower doses</u> tend to cause <u>minor damage</u> without <u>killing</u> the cells.
   This can give rise to <u>mutant cells</u> which <u>divide uncontrollably</u>. This is <u>cancer</u>.

3) <u>Higher doses</u> tend to <u>kill cells completely</u>, causing <u>radiation sickness</u> (leading to
   vomiting, tiredness and hair loss) if a lot of cells <u>all get affected at once</u>.

Irradiation and Contamination

Radioactive contamination comes about from touching and handling radioactive substances, whereas irradiation can result from just being near a source.

Exposure to Radiation is called Irradiation

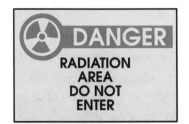

1) Objects near a radioactive source are irradiated by it. This simply means they're exposed to it (we're always being irradiated by background radiation sources).

2) Irradiating something does not make it radioactive.

3) Keeping sources in lead-lined boxes, standing behind barriers or being in a different room and using remote-controlled arms are all ways of reducing the effects of irradiation.

4) Radioactive materials can be used in some medical procedures. Patients are given the smallest possible dose of radiation necessary for their procedure to limit their exposure to it.

5) Medical staff who work with radiation wear photographic film badges to monitor their exposure.

Contamination is Radioactive Particles Getting onto Objects

1) If unwanted radioactive atoms get onto an object, the object is said to be contaminated. E.g. if you touch a radioactive source without wearing gloves, your hands would be contaminated.

2) These contaminating atoms might then decay, releasing radiation which could cause you harm.

3) Contamination is especially dangerous because radioactive particles could get inside your body.

4) Once a person is contaminated, they are at risk of harm until either the contamination is removed (which isn't always possible) or all the radioactive atoms have decayed.

5) Gloves and tongs should be used when handling sources, to avoid particles getting stuck to your skin or under your nails.

6) Some industrial workers wear protective suits to stop them breathing in particles.

Risk of Irradiation and Contamination Depends on the Radiation

1) Outside the body, beta and gamma radiation are the most dangerous, because they can penetrate the body and get to the delicate organs. Alpha is less dangerous, because it can't penetrate the skin.

2) Inside the body, alpha sources are the most dangerous. Alpha particles are strongly ionising, so they do all their damage in a very localised area. That means contamination, rather than irradiation, is the major concern when working with alpha sources.

Warm-Up & Exam Questions

Get your Geiger-Müller counters out — it looks like there's some serious brain activity ahead.
It's time to get stuck into some more radiation questions and start finishing this section off.

Warm-Up Questions

1) Give three sources of background radiation.
2) What does it mean if a radioactive source is said to have an activity of 1 becquerel?
3) Give an example of a detector that could be used to detect radiation.
4) A radioactive source has a half-life of three days.
   How long would it take for the source's activity to decrease by a factor of four?
5) What is the difference between radioactive contamination and irradiation?
6) Explain why you should wear gloves when handling radioactive materials.
7) Why is contamination by an alpha source more dangerous
   to humans than irradiation by an alpha source?

Exam Questions

1   Two different radioactive sources are being considered for use in a medical treatment.
    Their safety needs to be assessed.

   (a)   Give **two** possible effects of being exposed to a dose of ionising radiation.

                                                                                    [2 marks]

   Source A emits beta-minus radiation. Source B emits alpha radiation.

   (b)   Explain which of the sources presents a greater danger to patients whilst outside the body.

                                                                                    [1 mark]

   (c)   Suggest **one** precaution the hospital should take when storing radioactive substances.

                                                                                    [1 mark]

2   A radioactive sample has a half-life of 40 seconds.
    The initial activity of the sample is 8000 Bq.

   (a)   Calculate the activity after 2 minutes. Give your answer in becquerels.

                                                                                    [2 marks]

   (b)   Determine the number of half-lives it would take for the activity to fall to 250 Bq.

                                                                                    [2 marks]

   (c)   The radioactive source is left until its activity falls to 100 Bq.
         Calculate the final activity as a percentage of the initial activity.

                                                                                    [2 marks]

Revision Summary for Section 4

That's the end of <u>Section 4</u> — hopefully it wasn't too painful. Time to see how much you've absorbed.
- Try these questions and <u>tick off each one</u> when you <u>get it right</u>.
- When you've done <u>all the questions</u> under a heading, and are <u>completely happy</u> with it, tick it off.

The Atomic Model (p.71-73) ☑

1) Briefly describe how the model of an atom has changed over time. ☑
2) Describe the experiment that confirmed the existence of a small positively charged nucleus. ☑
3) Which has the lowest mass: a proton, an electron or a neutron? ☑
4) Draw a sketch to show our currently accepted model of the atom. ☑
5) True or false? Most of an atom's mass is contained within its nucleus. ☑
6) Describe the process of an electron moving to a higher energy level. ☑
7) What happens to an atom if it loses one or more of its outer electrons? ☑

Isotopes and Nuclear Decay (p.75-77) ☑

8) What is the atomic number of an atom? ☑
9) Which number defines what element an atom is: the atomic number or the mass number? ☑
10) How do isotopes of the same element differ? ☑
11) Name four things that may be emitted during radioactive decay. ☑
12) For alpha, beta and gamma radiation, give: a) their ionising power, b) their range in air. ☑
13) Which type of radiation has the same structure as a helium nucleus? ☑
14) What type of nuclear decay doesn't change the mass or charge of the nucleus? ☑

Half-life and the Dangers of Radiation (p.79-81) ☑

15) What is background radiation? ☑
16) True or false? It is possible to predict when a particular nucleus will decay. ☑
17) What is the activity of a source? What are its units? ☑
18) True or false? The half-life of a radioactive source decreases over time. ☑
19) Explain how you would find the half-life of a source, given a graph of its activity over time. ☑
20) Define irradiation and contamination. ☑
21) What precautions can be put in place to reduce contamination? ☑

Energy Transfers

Re-read pages 41-43. You'll need to remember everything on those pages for this section.

When a System Changes, Energy is Transferred

1) A system is just a fancy word for a single object (e.g. the air in a piston) or a group of objects (e.g. two colliding vehicles) that you're interested in. You can define your system to be anything you like.

2) When a system changes, energy is transferred. It can be transferred into or away from the system, between different objects in the system or between different types of energy stores (p.41).

3) Whenever a system changes, some energy is dissipated and stored in less useful ways (p.45).

4) The efficiency of a transfer is the proportion of the total energy supplied that ends up in useful energy stores (p.46).

5) You can use diagrams to show how efficient a transfer is, and which stores the energy is transferred to (see p.43 and 46).

6) How you define your system changes how you describe the energy transfers that take place (see below). A closed system is one that's defined so that the net change in energy is zero (p.42).

Energy can be Transferred by Heating...

1) A pan of water is heated on a gas camping stove.

2) When the system is the pan of water, energy is transferred into the system by heating to the thermal energy stores of the pan and the water, which increases their temperature.

3) When the system is the camping stove and the pan, energy is transferred within the system — from the chemical energy store of the gas to the thermal energy stores of the pan and the water, increasing their temperature.

...by Forces Doing Work...

1) A box is lifted up off of the floor. The box is the system.

2) As the box is lifted, work is done (see next page) against gravity.

3) This causes energy to be transferred to the box's kinetic and gravitational potential energy (GPE) stores.

If the box was dropped, the gravitational force would do work to transfer energy from the box's GPE store to its kinetic energy store.

...or by Electrical Equipment

1) Electrical devices work by transferring energy between different energy stores.

2) For example, electric irons transfer energy electrically from the mains power supply to the thermal energy store of their metal plates.

An electric toothbrush is a system. It transfers energy electrically from the chemical energy store of its battery to the kinetic energy store of its bristles.

Some of this energy is transferred out of the system to the surroundings by sound and by heating.

A hair dryer is a system. It transfers energy into the system electrically from the mains supply to the kinetic energy store of the fan inside of it.

It also transfers energy electrically to the thermal energy store of the heating element and some energy is transferred away from the system by sound.

Work Done

I'm sure you're no stranger to <u>doing work</u>, but in physics it's all to do with <u>forces</u> and <u>energy</u>.

If A Force **Moves** An Object, **Work is Done**

> When a <u>force</u> moves an object through a <u>distance</u>,
> <u>work is done</u> on the object and <u>energy is transferred</u>.

1) To make something <u>move</u>, some sort of <u>force</u> needs to act on it.
The thing <u>applying the force</u> needs a <u>source</u> of <u>energy</u> (like <u>fuel</u> or <u>food</u>).

2) The force does '<u>work</u>' to <u>move</u> the object and <u>energy</u> is
<u>transferred mechanically</u> from one <u>store</u> to another.

3) Remember, you can calculate the amount of energy in the <u>kinetic energy</u> and
<u>gravitational potential energy</u> stores using $\underline{KE = \frac{1}{2} \times m \times v^2}$ and $\underline{\Delta GPE = m \times g \times \Delta h}$ (p.41).

4) Whether energy is transferred '<u>usefully</u>' (e.g. <u>lifting a load</u>)
or is '<u>wasted</u>' (p.45) you can still say that '<u>work is done</u>'.

5) You can find out <u>how much</u> work has been done using:

$$E = F \times d$$

Work done (J) — Force (N) — Distance moved in the direction of the force (m)

6) <u>One joule of work</u> is done when a <u>force of one newton</u> causes an object to move a
<u>distance of one metre</u>. You can also write this as 1 J = 1 Nm (newton metre).

EXAMPLE:

A sled is pulled with a force of 10 N, for a distance of 4 m. Calculate the work done on the sled.

work done = force × distance = 10 × 4 = 40 J

The sled started at rest. After travelling 4 m, its final velocity is 4 m/s.
Calculate the sled's mass, assuming all the energy was transferred to the sled's kinetic energy store.

1) <u>Rearrange</u> the kinetic energy equation for m. $m = \dfrac{2 \times KE}{v^2}$

2) <u>Substitute</u> the values in. $= \dfrac{2 \times 40}{4^2} = 5 \text{ kg}$

Doing Work Often Causes a Rise in Temperature

1) A force doing work often causes a <u>rise in temperature</u> as energy is dissipated
to the <u>thermal</u> energy stores of a moving object and its surroundings.

2) This means that the process is often <u>wasteful</u> and so the <u>efficiency</u> of the process is <u>reduced</u>.
Remember, efficiency = $\dfrac{\text{useful energy transferred by the device}}{\text{total energy supplied to the device}}$ (p.46).

> When you push something along a <u>rough surface</u> (like a <u>carpet</u>) you are doing work <u>against frictional</u>
> <u>forces</u>. Energy is being <u>transferred</u> to the <u>kinetic energy store</u> of the <u>object</u> because it starts <u>moving</u>,
> but some is also being transferred to <u>thermal energy stores</u> due to the friction. This causes the
> overall <u>temperature</u> of the object to <u>increase</u>. (Like <u>rubbing your hands together</u> to warm them up.)

3) <u>Lubrication</u> (p.47) <u>reduces friction</u> and unwanted energy transfers to <u>thermal energy stores</u>.

Power

The <u>more powerful</u> a device is, the <u>more energy</u> it will transfer in a certain amount of <u>time</u>.

Power is How Much Work is Done per Second

1) <u>Power</u> is the <u>rate of energy transfer</u>.

2) The unit of power is the <u>watt</u> (<u>W</u>). 1 W = 1 J/s.

3) Remember, when <u>work is done</u>, <u>energy is transferred</u> (see previous page).

4) So, another way of describing power is how much <u>work</u> is being done <u>every second</u>.

5) This is the <u>very easy formula</u> for power:

$$\text{power (W)} = \frac{\text{work done (J)}}{\text{time taken (s)}} \qquad \text{or} \qquad P = \frac{E}{t}$$

The <u>larger</u> the <u>power</u> of an object, the <u>more</u> work it does per second. E.g. if an <u>electric heater</u> has a power of <u>600 W</u> this means it transfers <u>600 J</u> of energy <u>every second</u>. A <u>1200 W</u> heater would transfer <u>twice</u> as much energy per second and so would heat a room <u>quicker</u> than the 600 W heater.

EXAMPLE:

A microwave transfers 105 kJ of energy in 2 minutes. Find its power output.

1) <u>Convert</u> the values to the <u>correct units</u> first (p.12-13). 105 kJ = 105 000 J and 2 mins = 120 s

2) <u>Substitute</u> the values into the power equation. $P = E \div t = 105\ 000 \div 120 = 875\ \text{W}$

EXAMPLE:

A 300 W motor lifts a 50 kg mass 5 m vertically upwards. Calculate the amount of energy transferred to the gravitational potential energy store of the mass.

<u>Substitute</u> values into the equation for ΔGPE (p.41).

$\Delta\text{GPE} = m \times g \times \Delta h$
$= 50 \times 10 \times 5 = 2500\ \text{J}$

Calculate how long it takes the motor to lift the mass.

1) <u>Rearrange</u> the power equation for t. $\quad t = E \div P$

2) <u>Substitute</u> the values in. $\quad = 2500 \div 300 = 8.33...\ \text{s}$
$= 8\ \text{s (to 1 s.f.)}$

A large power doesn't always mean a large force...

A <u>powerful</u> device is not necessarily one which can exert a strong <u>force</u> (although it usually ends up that way). A <u>powerful</u> device is one which transfers <u>a lot of energy</u> in a <u>short space of time</u>.

Warm-Up & Exam Questions

Do some work by answering these questions and transfer some knowledge to your brain store.

Warm-Up Questions

1) What is meant by the word 'system'?

2) True or false? Energy can be transferred into a system.

3) Describe the useful energy transfer that occurs in a battery powered fan.

4) State the equation linking work done, force and distance moved in the direction of the force.

5) True or false? Power measures how quickly energy is transferred.

6) Which unit for power is equivalent to joules per second?

Exam Questions

1   A ball rolls down a ramp, as shown in **Figure 1**.

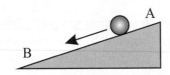

(a)   The ball and ramp are assumed to be a closed system.
Describe the energy transfer that takes place as the ball rolls
from point A to point B.

[2 marks]

Figure 1

(b)   State the change in total energy of the ball and ramp as this energy transfer occurs.

[1 mark]

2   The motor of an electric scooter moves the scooter 10 metres along a flat, horizontal
course in 20 seconds. During this time the motor does a total of 1000 J of work.

(a)   (i)   Write down the equation that links power, work done and time taken.

[1 mark]

(ii) Calculate the power of the motor.

[1 mark]

(b)   Whilst completing the course, 480 J of energy was transferred usefully to the
kinetic energy stores of the scooter and its rider. Calculate the efficiency of the scooter.

[2 marks]

(c)   The scooter's motor is replaced with a more powerful, but otherwise identical, motor.
It moves along the same 10 m course.
Describe how its performance will differ from before. Explain your answer.

[2 marks]

3   A train, initially at rest, moves 700 m in a straight line along a flat track.
The force acting on the train is 42 000 N forwards along the track.
You can assume there are no frictional forces acting on the train.
The train has a mass of 150 000 kg.

(a)   Calculate the work done by the force as the train moves 700 m. Give your answer in kJ.

[3 marks]

(b)   Assuming that all of this energy was transferred to the train's kinetic energy store,
calculate the final speed of the train.

[3 marks]

Forces

Force is a <u>vector</u> — it has both a <u>size</u> and a <u>direction</u> (unlike <u>scalar</u> quantities which only have a <u>size</u> — p.18). This means you can use <u>arrows</u> to represent the forces acting on an object or a system.

Interactions Between Objects Cause Forces

1) A <u>force</u> is a <u>push</u> or a <u>pull</u> on an object that is caused by it <u>interacting</u> with something.

2) Sometimes, objects need to be <u>touching</u> for a force to act. E.g. the <u>normal contact force</u> that acts between <u>all</u> touching objects, or <u>friction</u> between a car's <u>tyre</u> and the <u>road</u>. These are <u>contact forces</u>.

3) Other forces can act between objects that <u>aren't touching</u> (<u>non-contact forces</u>). They're usually caused by <u>interacting fields</u>. E.g. the <u>gravitational attraction</u> between objects (like the <u>Earth</u> and the <u>Sun</u>) is caused by their <u>gravitational fields</u> interacting.

4) <u>Interacting magnetic fields</u> (p.113) cause <u>attraction</u> or <u>repulsion</u> between <u>magnetic</u> objects, and the electrostatic force causing <u>attraction</u> and <u>repulsion</u> between <u>electrical charges</u> is due to interactions between their <u>electric fields</u>.

5) Whenever two objects <u>interact</u>, both objects feel an equal but opposite <u>force</u> (Newton's 3rd Law, p.26). This pair of forces is called an <u>interaction pair</u>. You can represent an interaction pair with a pair of <u>vectors</u> (<u>arrows</u>).

A <u>chair</u> exerts a force on the <u>ground</u>, whilst the ground pushes back at the chair with the <u>same</u> force (the <u>normal contact</u> force).

<u>Equal</u> but <u>opposite</u> forces are felt by <u>both</u> the chair and the ground.

This is <u>NOT</u> a free body force diagram (see below) — the forces are acting on <u>different objects</u>.

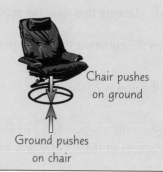

Chair pushes on ground

Ground pushes on chair

Free Body Force Diagrams Show All the Forces Acting on Objects

1) A <u>free body force diagram</u> shows an <u>isolated body</u> (an object or system on its own), and <u>all</u> the <u>forces</u> acting on it.

2) It should include <u>every</u> force acting <u>on the body</u>, but <u>none</u> of the forces it <u>exerts</u> on the rest of the world.

3) The <u>sizes</u> of the arrows show the <u>relative magnitudes</u> of the forces and the <u>directions</u> show the directions of the forces.

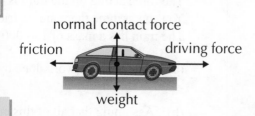

normal contact force

friction   driving force

weight

Resultant Forces

The resultant force acting on an object is found by adding together or subtracting all the forces acting on it.

A Resultant Force is the Overall Force on a Point or Object

1) In most real situations there are at least two forces acting on an object along any direction.

2) If you have a number of forces acting at a single point, you can replace them with a single force (so long as the single force has the same effect as all the original forces together).

3) This single force is called the resultant force (or sometimes the net force on an object).

4) If the forces all act along the same line (they're all parallel), the overall effect is found by adding those going in the same direction and subtracting any going in the opposite direction.

5) Objects in equilibrium have a resultant force of zero — see the next page. Objects in equilibrium are either stationary, or moving at a steady speed (this is Newton's 1st Law — p.25).

- The normal contact force felt by the car is equal to its weight. These forces act in opposite directions, so there is no resultant force in the vertical direction (1500 N – 1500 N = 0 N).
- The frictional force acting on the car is smaller than the driving force pushing it forward, so there is a resultant force in the horizontal direction.
- 1200 N – 1000 N = 200 N. The resultant force is 200 N (to the left).

Use Scale Drawings to Find Resultant Forces

Scale drawings can help you resolve forces (see next page) or work out the resultant force.

1) Draw all the forces acting on an object, to scale, 'tip-to-tail'.

2) Then draw a straight line from the start of the first force to the end of the last force — this is the resultant (or net) force.

3) Measure the length of the resultant force on the diagram to find the magnitude of the force and the angle to find its direction.

Make sure the scale you use is sensible. You want large, clear diagrams that make your calculations easier to do.

EXAMPLE:

A man is on an electric bicycle that has a driving force of 4 N north.
However, the wind produces a force of 3 N east. Find the net force acting on the man.

1) Start by drawing a scale drawing of the forces acting.

2) Make sure you choose a sensible scale (e.g. 1 cm = 1 N).

3) Draw the net force from the tail of the first arrow to the tip of the last arrow.

4) Measure the length of the net force with a ruler and use the scale to find the force in N.

5) Use a protractor to measure the direction as a bearing.

A bearing is an angle measured clockwise from north, given as a 3-digit number, e.g. 10° = 010°.

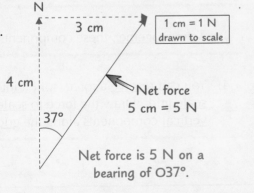

Net force is 5 N on a bearing of 037°.

When it comes to scale drawings, bigger is better...

If you're asked to draw a scale drawing in an exam, try to use up as much of the space provided as possible. This will help you to measure angles and lengths more accurately.

Resolving Forces

So, several forces can be <u>added tip-to-tail</u> to give a single <u>resultant force</u>. Sometimes it's helpful to reverse this process and <u>split up</u> a single force into components — this is known as <u>resolving a force</u>.

An Object is in **Equilibrium** if the **Forces** on it are **Balanced**

1) If <u>all</u> of the forces acting on an object <u>combine</u> to give a resultant force of <u>zero</u>, the object is in <u>equilibrium</u>.

2) On a <u>scale diagram</u>, this means that the <u>tip</u> of the <u>last</u> force you draw should end where the <u>tail</u> of the first <u>force</u> you drew begins.

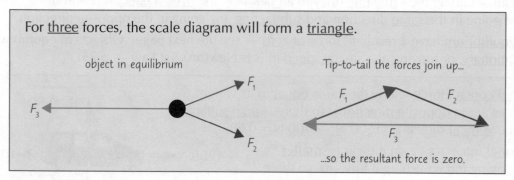

For <u>three</u> forces, the scale diagram will form a <u>triangle</u>.

object in equilibrium

F_1

F_3

F_2

Tip-to-tail the forces join up...

F_1 F_2

F_3

...so the resultant force is zero.

3) You might be <u>given</u> forces acting on an <u>object</u> and told to <u>find</u> a <u>missing force</u>, given that the object is in <u>equilibrium</u>.

4) To do this, draw out the forces you <u>do</u> know (to <u>scale</u> and <u>tip-to-tail</u>), then <u>join</u> the <u>end</u> of the <u>last force</u> to the <u>start</u> of the <u>first force</u>. Make sure you draw this last force in the <u>right direction</u> — it's in the <u>opposite</u> direction to how you'd draw a <u>resultant</u> force.

5) This line is the <u>missing force</u>, you can measure its <u>size</u> and <u>direction</u>.

You Can **Split** a Force into **Components**

1) Not <u>all</u> forces act <u>horizontally</u> or <u>vertically</u> — some act at <u>awkward angles</u>.

2) To make these <u>easier</u> to deal with, they can be <u>split</u> into two <u>components</u> at <u>right angles</u> to each other (usually horizontal and vertical).

3) Acting <u>together</u>, these components have the <u>same effect</u> as the single force.

4) You can <u>resolve</u> a force (split it into components) by drawing it on a <u>scale grid</u>. Draw the force <u>to scale</u>, and then add the <u>horizontal</u> and <u>vertical</u> components along the <u>gridlines</u>. Then you can just <u>measure</u> them.

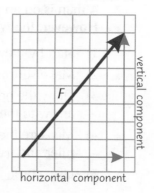

F

vertical component

horizontal component

You might be given a scale to work with...

MATHS TIP

You've seen how <u>useful</u> scale drawings are over the last couple of pages, so you need to make sure you're happy using scales. Let's say your scale is 1 cm = 3 N. To find the size of a <u>force</u> from its arrow length, <u>multiply the arrow length by 3</u> (e.g. a 5 cm arrow would represent a 15 N force). To find the arrow length of a force, <u>divide the force by 3</u> (e.g. a 30 N force is a 10 cm arrow).

Warm-Up & Exam Questions

Time to test your ability to force new information into your mind. That's right, there's more questions. Work through the warm-ups and when you're feeling happy with them, dive into the exam questions.

Warm-Up Questions

1) True or false? Objects can only exert a force on one another if they are touching.
2) What does the length of an arrow on a free body diagram represent?
3) What is meant by the resultant force acting on an object?
4) If an object is equilibrium, what will you find if you draw all the forces acting on it, to scale and tip-to-tail?

Exam Questions

1   **Figure 1** shows two hot air balloons, labelled with the forces acting on them.   *Grade 4-6*

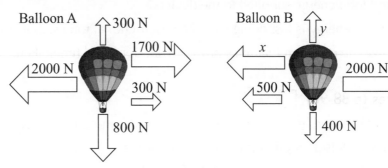

Figure 1

(a)   Calculate the size of the resultant force acting on Balloon A and give its direction.

[3 marks]

(b)   The resultant force acting on Balloon B is zero. Calculate the size of forces *x* and *y*.

[2 marks]

2   An apple is blown out of a tree on a windy day. As it falls, the wind exerts a force of 0.5 N horizontally on the apple.   *Grade 6-7*
Gravity exerts a force of 1.2 N vertically downwards on the apple. These forces are shown in **Figure 2**.

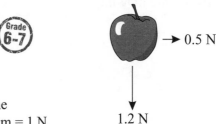

(a)   (i)   Using a scale drawing, determine the magnitude of the resultant force acting on the apple. Use a scale of 5 cm = 1 N.

[3 marks]   **Figure 2**

(ii)   Determine the angle the resultant force makes with the vertical downwards direction.

[1 mark]

(b)   The force the apple experiences due to gravity is an example of a non-contact interaction. Give **one** more example of a non-contact interaction.

[1 mark]

Revision Summary for Section 5

That's <u>Section 5</u> done and dusted — now you've got a chance to see <u>how much has stuck</u>.

• Try these questions and <u>tick off each one</u> when you <u>get it right</u>.

• When you've done <u>all the questions</u> under a heading and are <u>completely happy</u> with it, tick it off.

Energy Transfers, Work Done and Power (p.84-86) ☑

1) True or false? When a system changes, energy is transferred. ☑

2) Energy may be transferred electrically or by heating. Name a third way of transferring energy. ☑

3) Give the equation that links kinetic energy, mass and speed. ☑

4) Give the equation that links change in gravitational potential energy,
   mass, gravitational field strength and change in vertical height. ☑

5) Work done can be measured in joules or newton metres.
   How many joules is one newton metre equivalent to? ☑

6) True or false? A force doing work can cause a rise in temperature. ☑

7) Give the equation that links efficiency, useful energy transferred by the device
   and total energy supplied to the device. ☑

8) Often, energy is lost doing work against frictional forces. Suggest a way to reduce friction. ☑

9) Give the equation that links power, work done and time taken. ☑

Forces (p.88-90) ☑

10) Explain the difference between contact and non-contact forces. ☑

11) True or false? Friction is a non-contact force. ☑

12) What force causes the repulsion of two like electrical charges? What causes this force? ☑

13) What is a free body force diagram? ☑

14) Describe how you would use a scale diagram to work out the resultant force acting on an object. ☑

15) True or false? The arrows on a scale diagram for the forces on an object in equilibrium
    join up to create a closed shape. ☑

16) Describe how you would resolve a force into horizontal and vertical components
    using a scale drawing. ☑

Circuit Basics

Current, potential difference and resistance are key to understanding circuits. But first up, circuit symbols.

Circuit Symbols You Should **Know**

You need to be able to use these symbols to interpret and draw circuit diagrams.

There's more about a.c. and d.c. on p.108.

cell	battery	open switch	closed switch	filament lamp	fuse	LED	power supply
—||—	—||--||—	—o⁄o—	—o–o—	—⊗—	—▭—	—(▷|)↗↗—	d.c. —o⁻ o⁺— a.c. —o∼o—

resistor	variable resistor	ammeter	voltmeter	diode	LDR	thermistor	motor
—▭—	—▱⁄—	—(A)—	—(V)—	—(▷|)—	↘↘(▯)—	—▱—	—(M)—

Current is the **Flow** of **Electrical Charge**

1) Current is the flow of electric charge (e.g. electrons, see below) around the circuit.

2) The unit of current is the ampere, A.

3) Potential difference (or voltage) is the driving force that pushes the charge round.

4) The unit of potential difference is the volt, V.

5) Resistance is anything that slows the flow down.

6) The unit of resistance is the ohm, Ω.

7) Current will only flow through an electrical component if there is a potential difference across that component, and if the circuit is closed (complete).

8) The current flowing through a component depends on the potential difference across it and the resistance of the component (p.95).

9) Generally speaking, the higher the potential difference across a component, the higher the current will be. And the greater the resistance of a component, the smaller the current that flows (for a given potential difference across the component). There's more on resistance on p.95.

potential difference of supply provides the 'push'

+ve −ve

R

current flows

resistance — opposes the flow

Current in **Metals** is the Flow of **Free Electrons**

1) All atoms contain positive protons and neutral neutrons in the nucleus, with negatively charged electrons orbiting the nucleus (p.72).

2) The atoms in metals are bonded in such a way that metals are made up of a lattice (a grid) of positive ions (p.73) surrounded by free electrons.

3) These electrons are free to move through the whole metal. The current in metals is the flow of these free electrons.

positive ion

free electron

Electrons flow the opposite way to the current...

Electrons in circuits actually move from −ve to +ve, but it's conventional to draw current as though it's flowing from +ve to −ve. It's what early physicists thought (before they discovered electrons), and it's stuck.

Circuit Basics

Charges <u>transfer energy</u> round a circuit — you can work out <u>how much</u> with a couple of equations...

Total Charge Through a Circuit Depends on Current and Time

1) <u>Current</u> is the <u>rate of flow</u> of <u>charge</u>.

2) If a <u>current</u> (*I*) flows past a point in a circuit for a length of <u>time</u> (*t*), then the <u>charge</u> (*Q*) that has passed this point is given by this formula:

$$\text{charge} = \text{current} \times \text{time} \qquad \text{or} \qquad Q = I \times t$$

More charge passes around the circuit in a given time when a greater current flows.

3) To use this formula, you need <u>current</u> in <u>amperes</u>, A, <u>charge</u> in <u>coulombs</u>, C, and <u>time</u> in <u>seconds</u>, s.

> **EXAMPLE:**
>
> **A battery charger passes 18 000 C of charge to a battery over a period of 2.5 hours. Calculate the current flowing between the battery charger and the battery.**
>
> 1) <u>Convert</u> the time into seconds. $2.5 \times 60 \times 60 = 9000$ s
> 2) <u>Rearrange</u> the equation for current. $I = Q \div t$
> 3) <u>Substitute</u> into the rearranged equation. $= 18\,000 \div 9000 = 2$ A

Potential Difference is the Energy Transferred Per Unit Charge

1) The <u>potential difference</u> is the <u>energy transferred per coulomb of charge</u> that passes between <u>two points</u> in an electrical circuit.

2) You can calculate energy transferred (*E*), from charge moved (*Q*), and potential difference (*V*), using <u>this formula</u>:

$$\text{energy transferred} = \text{charge moved} \times \text{potential difference} \qquad \text{or} \qquad E = Q \times V$$

3) To use this formula, you need <u>energy transferred</u> in <u>joules</u>, J, <u>charge moved</u> in <u>coulombs</u>, C, and <u>potential difference</u> in <u>volts</u>, V.

4) So, the <u>potential difference</u> (p.d.) across an electrical component is the <u>amount of energy</u> transferred by that electrical component (e.g. the amount of energy transferred by a motor to its kinetic energy store) <u>per unit charge</u> passed. One <u>volt</u> is one <u>joule per coulomb</u>.

5) Potential difference is sometimes called <u>voltage</u>. They're the same thing.

> **EXAMPLE:**
>
> **The motor in an electric toothbrush is attached to a 3 V battery. 140 C of charge passes through the circuit as it is used. Calculate the energy transferred.**
>
> $E = Q \times V = 140 \times 3 = 420$ J

Understanding potential difference is potentially difficult...

<u>Potential difference</u> can be harder to visualise than current or resistance. As long as you're happy with the <u>definition</u> for p.d. on this page and are comfortable using the <u>equations</u>, you can't go far wrong.

Potential Difference and Resistance

Prepare yourself to meet one of the most <u>important equations</u> in electronics. It's all about <u>resistance</u>, <u>current</u> and <u>potential difference</u>... Now if that doesn't tempt you on to read this page, I don't know what will.

Resistance, Potential Difference and Current: $V = I \times R$

1) <u>Potential difference</u> (V), <u>current</u> (I), and <u>resistance</u> (R) are all related through this formula:

potential difference = current × resistance   or $V = I \times R$

2) To use this formula, you need <u>potential difference</u> in <u>volts</u>, V, <u>current</u> in <u>amperes</u>, A, and <u>resistance</u> in <u>ohms</u>, Ω.

3) If you <u>rearrange</u> this equation, you can use it to calculate the <u>resistance</u> of a component from measurements of <u>potential difference</u> and <u>current</u> (e.g. from the experiment on the next page).

EXAMPLE:

A 4.0 Ω resistor in a circuit has a potential difference of 6.0 V across it. What is the current through the resistor?

1) <u>Rearrange</u> the equation for current. $I = V \div R$

2) <u>Substitute</u> into the rearranged equation. $= 6.0 \div 4.0 = 1.5$ A

Resistance Increases with Temperature (Usually)

1) When an electrical charge flows through a component, it has to <u>do work against resistance</u>.

2) This causes an <u>electrical transfer of energy</u> (work done = energy transferred, p.85).

3) Some of this energy is transferred <u>usefully</u> but some of it is <u>dissipated</u> to the <u>thermal</u> energy stores of the <u>component</u> and the <u>surroundings</u>.

4) So when a <u>current</u> flows through a <u>resistor</u>, the resistor <u>heats up</u>.

5) This happens because the <u>electrons collide with the ions</u> in the lattice that make up the resistor as they flow through it.

6) This gives the ions <u>energy</u>, which causes them to <u>vibrate</u> more (and the energy in the <u>thermal energy store</u> of the <u>resistor</u> to increase — see p.125).

7) The more the ions vibrate, the <u>harder</u> it is for electrons to get through the resistor (because there are more collisions).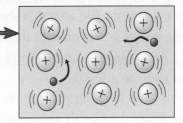

8) So for a <u>given p.d.</u> the current <u>decreases</u> as the resistor <u>heats up</u>.

9) If the resistor gets <u>too hot</u>, <u>no</u> current will be able to flow.

10) There is one <u>exception</u> to this — the resistance of a <u>thermistor decreases</u> with an increase in temperature (p.97).

11) <u>Low resistance wires</u> (p.120) can be used to <u>reduce</u> the <u>energy dissipated</u> to thermal stores as the current flows between components.

The more ions vibrate, the lower the current passing through...

A <u>resistor</u> will <u>heat up</u> as <u>current</u> flows through it. As a resistor heats up, it becomes <u>more difficult</u> for current to <u>flow</u>. Make sure you can explain why this is in terms of the <u>electrons</u> and <u>ions</u> in the circuit.

 # Investigating Components

Time for a <u>practical</u> — the <u>set-up</u> described on this page can be used to <u>investigate any component</u>. Handy.

You Can **Investigate** How **P.d.** Changes with **Current**

To investigate the <u>relationship</u> between <u>current</u> (I), <u>p.d.</u> (V) and <u>resistance</u> (R) for a range of components, such as a <u>filament bulb</u> or a <u>fixed resistor</u>:

1) Set up the <u>test circuit</u> as shown below.

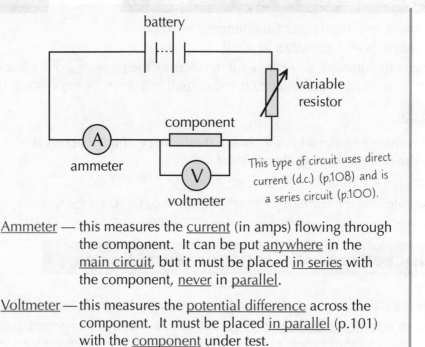

Ammeter — this measures the <u>current</u> (in amps) flowing through the component. It can be put <u>anywhere</u> in the main circuit, but it must be placed <u>in series</u> with the component, <u>never</u> in <u>parallel</u>.

Voltmeter — this measures the <u>potential difference</u> across the component. It must be placed <u>in parallel</u> (p.101) with the <u>component</u> under test.

2) The <u>variable resistor</u> is used to <u>change</u> the <u>current</u> in the circuit.

3) As $I = V \div R$ (p.95), <u>increasing</u> the resistance of the variable resistor <u>lowers</u> the current through the circuit at a fixed supply p.d.. This changes the <u>potential difference</u> across the <u>component</u>.

4) Now you need to get <u>sets</u> of <u>current</u> and <u>potential difference</u> readings:

- Set the <u>resistance</u> of the variable resistor.
- Measure the <u>current</u> through and <u>potential difference</u> across the component.
- Take measurements at a number of <u>different</u> resistances.

5) <u>Swap</u> over the wires connected to the cell to reverse the <u>direction of the current</u>. The ammeter should now display <u>negative readings</u>.

6) <u>Repeat</u> step 4 to get results for negative values of current.

7) <u>Plot</u> the <u>current</u> against the <u>potential difference</u> to get I-V graphs like the ones on the next page.

8) You can use this data to work out the component's <u>resistance</u> for <u>each measurement</u> of I and V, using the formula on p.95, so you can see if the resistance of the component <u>changes</u> as I and V change.

9) Make sure the circuit doesn't get <u>too hot</u> over the course of your experiment, as this will mess up your results (see previous page). If the circuit starts to warm up, <u>disconnect</u> it for a while between readings so it can cool down. And, like any experiment, you should do repeats and <u>calculate means</u>.

Have a look at page 9 for more about calculating averages and interpreting your results.

WORKING SCIENTIFICALLY

In this experiment, temperature is a control variable...

The <u>temperature</u> of the component needs to be kept <u>constant</u>, otherwise the investigation would not be a <u>fair test</u>. Variables that need to be kept the same are called <u>control variables</u> (page 6).

Circuit Devices

With your current and your potential difference measured, you can now make some <u>sweet</u> graphs...

Three Important **Current-Potential Difference Graphs**

<u>I-V graphs</u> show how the <u>current</u> varies as you <u>change</u> the <u>potential difference</u> (p.d.).
Here are three examples, plotted from the <u>experiment</u> on the previous page:

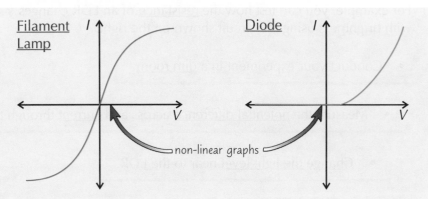

Fixed Resistors — linear graphs

Current is directly proportional to p.d. (if the temperature stays the same). Different resistors have different resistances, so their I-V graphs have different slopes.

Filament Lamp — non-linear graphs

The increasing current increases the temperature of the filament, which makes the resistance increase (p.95) so their I-V graphs are curved.

Diode — non-linear graphs

Current will only flow through a diode in one direction, as shown. The diode has very high resistance in the opposite direction. Current flows this way through a diode:

1) <u>Linear</u> components have an *I-V* graph that's a <u>straight line</u> (e.g. a fixed resistor).
<u>Non-linear</u> components have a <u>curved</u> *I-V* graph (e.g. a filament lamp or a diode).

2) For <u>linear</u> components, if the line goes through <u>(0,0)</u>, the resistance of the component equals the <u>inverse</u> of the <u>gradient</u> of the line, or "<u>1/gradient</u>". The <u>steeper</u> the graph, the <u>lower</u> the resistance.

3) You can find the <u>resistance</u> for <u>any point</u> on any *I-V* graph by reading the <u>p.d.</u> and <u>current</u> at that point and sticking them into $V = I \times R$ (p.95).

LDR is Short for **Light Dependent Resistor**

1) An LDR is a resistor that is <u>dependent</u> on the <u>intensity</u> of <u>light</u>. Simple really.

2) In <u>bright light</u>, the resistance <u>falls</u>.

3) In <u>darkness</u>, the resistance is <u>highest</u>.

4) They have lots of applications including <u>automatic night lights</u>, outdoor lighting and <u>burglar detectors</u>.

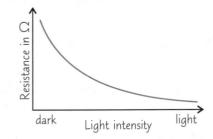

A **Thermistor's** Resistance Decreases as **Temperature Increases**

1) A <u>thermistor</u> is a <u>temperature dependent</u> resistor.

2) For <u>negative temperature coefficient</u> thermistors:
   - Their resistance <u>drops</u> in <u>hotter</u> conditions.
   - Their resistance <u>goes up</u> in <u>cooler</u> conditions.

3) Thermistors make useful <u>temperature detectors</u>, e.g. <u>car engine</u> temperature sensors and electronic <u>thermostats</u>.

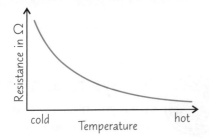

Investigating LDRs and Thermistors

Whip out the ammeter, I feel another <u>experiment</u> coming on — this time it's <u>thermistors</u> and <u>LDRs</u>.

You can **Investigate** How **Resistance** Changes for **LDRs**

1) You can create <u>*I-V* graphs</u> for <u>LDRs</u> using the method on p.96.
2) But the <u>resistance</u> of LDRs can <u>depend on</u> things <u>other than</u> current.
3) For example, you can test how the <u>resistance</u> of an LDR changes with brightness using the circuit shown on the right:

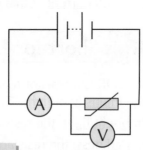

- Conduct your experiment in a <u>dim room</u>.

- Measure the <u>potential difference</u> across and <u>current</u> through the LDR.

- <u>Change the light level</u> near to the LDR.

- Measure the <u>p.d.</u> and <u>current</u> again. <u>Repeat</u> this for a <u>range</u> of light levels.

- Calculate the <u>resistance</u> for each measurement using $R = V \div I$.

4) You should find that as the light level gets <u>brighter</u>, the <u>current</u> through the LDR <u>increases</u> as the <u>resistance decreases</u>.

You can **Investigate** How **Resistance** Changes for **Thermistors**

1) As with LDRs, you can use the method on p.96 to create <u>*I-V* graphs</u> for <u>thermistors</u>.
2) Also, you can test how the <u>resistance</u> of a thermistor changes with <u>temperature</u> using the circuit on the right:

- Measure the <u>p.d. across</u> and <u>current through</u> the thermistor.

- <u>Change the temperature</u> of the thermistor by heating it.

- Measure the <u>current</u> and <u>p.d.</u> for a range of <u>different temperatures</u>.

- Calculate the <u>resistance</u> for each measurement using $R = V \div I$.

3) You should find that as the <u>temperature increases</u>, the <u>current</u> through the thermistor <u>increases</u> — showing that the <u>resistance decreases</u>.

Warm-Up & Exam Questions

Now you've had an intro to some circuit basics, check you've understood it all by trying these questions.

Warm-Up Questions

1) Draw the symbol for an LED.
2) What are the units of resistance?
3) True or false? Current in metals is the flow of positive ions.
4) State the equation linking energy transferred, charged moved and potential difference.
5) Explain, in terms of electrons and ions, why energy is transferred to a resistor's thermal energy store when a current flows through it.
6) How should a voltmeter be connected in a circuit to measure the p.d. across a component?
7) Sketch the current-potential difference graph for a filament lamp.
8) How does a thermistor's resistance change as the temperature of its surroundings increases?

Exam Questions

1   **Figure 1** shows a circuit diagram for a standard test circuit. When the switch is closed, the ammeter reads 0.30 A and the voltmeter reads 1.5 V.

   (a) (i) The switch is closed for 35 seconds. Calculate the total charge that flows through the filament lamp during this time.

                                                [2 marks]

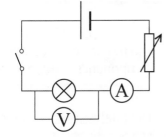

Figure 1

      (ii) Calculate the energy transferred to the filament lamp during this time.

                                                [2 marks]

   (b) The variable resistor is used to increase the resistance in the test circuit. State how this will affect the current flowing through the circuit.

                                                [1 mark]

PRACTICAL

2   A student carried out an experiment to measure what happened to the potential difference across a diode as the current through it was varied. **Figure 2** shows a graph of her results.

   (a) State **one** variable that should be controlled in this experiment.

                                                [1 mark]

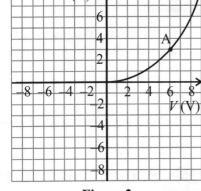

Figure 2

   (b) Calculate the resistance of the diode at the point marked A in **Figure 2**.

                                                [4 marks]

Series Circuits

You'll need to make sure you know the <u>rules</u> for <u>current</u> and <u>p.d.</u> in series circuits. You also need to be able to explain what happens to a circuit's <u>total resistance</u> when you connect <u>resistors</u> in <u>series</u>.

Series Circuits — All or Nothing

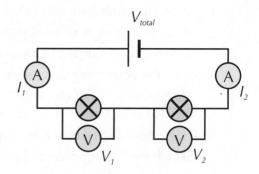

1) In <u>series circuits</u>, the different components are connected <u>in a line</u>, <u>end to end</u>, between the +ve and –ve of the power supply (except for <u>voltmeters</u>, which are always connected <u>in parallel</u>, but they don't count as part of the circuit).

2) If you remove or disconnect <u>one</u> component, the circuit is <u>broken</u> and they all <u>stop working</u>. This is generally <u>not very handy</u>, and in practice <u>very few things</u> are connected in series.

3) You can use the following rules to <u>design</u> series circuits to <u>measure quantities</u> and test components. For a <u>series</u> circuit:

- There's a bigger <u>supply p.d.</u> when more cells are in series (if they're all <u>connected</u> the <u>same way</u>). E.g. when two cells with a p.d. of 1.5 V are <u>connected in series</u> they supply 3 V <u>between them</u>.

- The <u>current</u> is the <u>same everywhere</u>. $I_1 = I_2$ etc. The size of the current depends on the <u>total p.d.</u> and the <u>total resistance</u> of the circuit ($I = V \div R$).

- The total <u>potential difference</u> of the supply is <u>shared</u> between components. The p.d. for each component depends on its <u>resistance</u>. The <u>bigger</u> a component's <u>resistance</u>, the bigger its <u>share</u> of the <u>total potential difference</u>.

- The <u>total resistance</u> of the circuit <u>increases</u> as you <u>add</u> resistors (see below).

Adding Resistors in Series Increases Total Resistance

1) In series circuits the <u>total resistance</u> of two components is just the <u>sum</u> of their resistances.

2) This is because by <u>adding a resistor</u> in series, the two resistors have to <u>share</u> the total p.d..

3) The potential difference across each resistor is <u>lower</u>, so the <u>current</u> through each resistor is also lower. In a series circuit, the current is the <u>same everywhere</u> so the total current in the circuit is <u>reduced</u> when a resistor is added. This means the total <u>resistance</u> of the circuit <u>increases</u>.

EXAMPLE:

For the circuit diagram shown,
calculate the total resistance of the circuit.

$R_{total} = 2 + 3 = 5 \, \Omega$

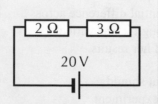

 ## A quick way to check your p.d. calculations...

The <u>ratio</u> in which <u>p.d.</u> is shared out between components in series is the same as the <u>ratio</u> of their <u>resistances</u>. So if a resistor has a resistance <u>three times</u> greater than a light bulb, the resistor will receive a share of the battery's p.d. that is <u>three times</u> larger than that received by the bulb.

Parallel Circuits

Parallel circuits can be a little bit trickier to wrap your head around, but they're much more useful than series circuits. Most electronics use a combination of series and parallel circuitry.

Parallel Circuits — Everything is Independent

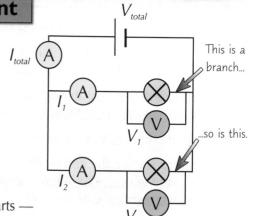

This is a branch...

...so is this.

1) In parallel circuits, each component is separately connected to the +ve and –ve of the supply (except ammeters, which are always connected in series).

2) If you remove or disconnect one of them, it will hardly affect the others at all.

3) This is obviously how most things must be connected, for example in cars and in household electrics. You have to be able to switch everything on and off separately.

4) Everyday circuits often include a mixture of series and parallel parts — when looking at components on the same branch the rules for series circuits apply.

Potential Difference in Parallel Circuits

1) In parallel circuits all components get the full source p.d., so the voltage is the same across all components: $\longrightarrow$ $\boxed{V_1 = V_2 = V_3 = ...}$

2) This means that identical bulbs connected in parallel will all be at the same brightness.

Current in Parallel Circuits

1) In parallel circuits the current is shared between branches.

2) The total current flowing around the circuit is equal to the total of all the currents through the separate components: $\longrightarrow$ $\boxed{I_{total} = I_1 + I_2 + ...}$

3) In a parallel circuit, there are junctions where the current either splits or rejoins. The total current going into a junction has to equal the total current leaving it.

4) If two identical components are connected in parallel then the same current will flow through each component.

Adding a Resistor in Parallel Reduces the Total Resistance

1) If you have two resistors in parallel, their total resistance is less than the resistance of the smallest of the two resistors.

2) This can be tough to get your head around, but think about it like this:

- In parallel, both resistors have the same potential difference across them as the source.
- This means the 'pushing force' making the current flow is the same as the source potential difference for each resistor that you add.
- But by adding another loop, the current has more than one direction to go in.
- This increases the total current that can flow around the circuit. Using $V = I \times R$, an increase in current means a decrease in the total resistance of the circuit.

Learn the difference between series and parallel circuits...

In series circuits, current is the same everywhere and p.d. is split between components. In parallel circuits, p.d. is the same across each branch and current is split between branches. Don't forget that, it's important.

Investigating Circuits

Here's an <u>experiment</u> to see how placing <u>components</u> in series or parallel can affect a circuit's total resistance.

You Can **Investigate** Adding **Resistors** in **Series**...

1) First, you'll need to find at least four <u>identical resistors</u>.

2) Then build the circuit shown on the right using <u>one</u> of the resistors. Make a note of the <u>potential difference</u> of the <u>battery</u> (V).

3) Measure the <u>current</u> through the circuit using the ammeter. Use this to <u>calculate the total resistance</u> of the circuit using $R = V \div I$.

4) Add another <u>resistor</u>, in <u>series</u> with the first.

5) Again, measure the current through the circuit and use this and the <u>potential difference</u> of the battery to <u>calculate</u> the <u>total resistance</u> of the circuit.

6) Repeat <u>steps 4 and 5</u> until you've added all of your resistors.

7) <u>Plot a graph</u> of the <u>number of resistors</u> against the <u>total resistance</u> of the circuit (see below).

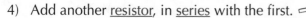

... or in **Parallel**

1) Using the <u>same equipment</u> as before (so the experiment is a <u>fair test</u>), build the same <u>initial circuit</u>.

2) Measure the <u>total current</u> through the circuit and <u>calculate the total resistance</u> of the circuit using $R = V \div I$ (again, V is the potential difference of the <u>battery</u>).

3) Next, add another <u>resistor</u>, in <u>parallel</u> with the first.

4) Measure the <u>total current</u> through the circuit and use this and the <u>potential difference</u> of the battery to calculate the <u>total resistance of the circuit</u>.

5) Repeat <u>steps 3 and 4</u> until you've added all of your resistors.

6) Plot a <u>graph</u> of the <u>number of resistors</u> in the circuit against the <u>total resistance</u>.

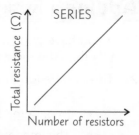

Your Results Should **Match** the **Resistance Rules**

You should find that adding resistors in <u>series increases</u> the total <u>resistance</u> of the circuit (adding a resistor <u>decreases</u> the total <u>current</u> through the circuit).

The <u>more</u> resistors you add, the <u>larger</u> the resistance of the whole circuit.

If you measured the <u>p.d.</u> across one of the resistors, you would find the p.d. <u>decreases</u> as more resistors are added in series.

When you add resistors in <u>parallel</u>, the <u>total current</u> through the circuit <u>increases</u> — so the total resistance of the circuit has <u>decreased</u>.

The <u>more</u> resistors you add, the <u>smaller</u> the overall resistance becomes.

If you measured the <u>p.d.</u> across one of the resistors, you would find the p.d. <u>remains the same</u> regardless of how many resistors are added in parallel.

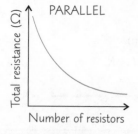

You can also do the experiments on this page with <u>filament lamps</u> instead of resistors:
- The lamps should get <u>dimmer</u> when a lamp is added in <u>series</u> (as the p.d. is being <u>shared out</u>).
- The lamps should be the <u>same brightness</u> in <u>parallel</u> (as they each have the <u>same p.d.</u>).

Warm-Up & Exam Questions

Time to see what you can remember about parallel and series circuits.

Warm-Up Questions

1) True or false? Current is the same everywhere in a series circuit.

2) How is the total resistance of a series circuit calculated from the resistance of each component in the circuit?

3) Two identical resistors are connected in parallel across a 3 V cell.
   What is the potential difference across each resistor?

4) Which circuit has the higher total resistance: two resistors connected in series,
   or the same two resistors connected in parallel?

5) Describe an experiment that could be used to investigate how increasing the number of resistors connected in series affects the total resistance of a circuit.

Exam Questions

1   **Figure 1** shows a series circuit.   *(Grade 4-6)*

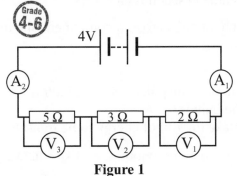

Figure 1

(a)   Calculate the total resistance in the circuit.

[1 mark]

(b)   The reading on A_1 is 0.4 A.
      Explain what the reading on A_2 is.

[2 marks]

(c) V_1 reads 0.8 V and V_2 reads 1.2 V.
      Calculate the reading on V_3.

[1 mark]

2   A parallel circuit is connected as shown in **Figure 2**.   *(Grade 7-9)*

(a)   Find the reading on voltmeter V_1.

[1 mark]

(b)   Calculate the reading on ammeter A_1.

[3 marks]

(c)   Calculate the reading on ammeter A_2.

[1 mark]

(d)   A third resistor is added to the circuit,
      connected in series with the 3 Ω resistor.
      Explain how this would affect the reading on A_2.

[3 marks]

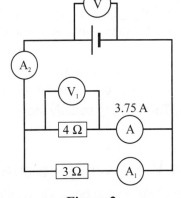

Figure 2

Energy in Circuits

You can think about <u>electrical circuits</u> in terms of <u>energy transfer</u> — the charge carriers take energy around the circuit. When they go through an electrical component energy is transferred to make the component work.

Energy Transferred Depends on Current, p.d. and Time

1) When an electrical <u>charge</u> goes through a <u>change</u> in potential difference, then <u>energy</u> is <u>transferred</u> (as <u>work</u> is done <u>against resistance</u> — p.95).

2) Energy is <u>supplied</u> to the charge at the <u>power source</u> to 'raise' it through a potential.

3) The charge <u>gives up</u> this energy when it 'falls' through any <u>potential drop</u> in <u>components</u> elsewhere in the circuit.

4) To find the <u>energy transferred</u> to an electrical component, you can use the equation:

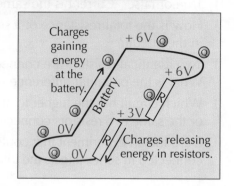

$$E = I \times V \times t$$

This equation comes from combining the two equations from p.94.

Where E is energy transferred in joules (J), I is current in amps (A), V is p.d. in volts (V) and t is time in seconds (s).

5) The <u>larger</u> the <u>current</u> through, or <u>p.d. across</u>, a component, the more <u>energy</u> is transferred to it.

EXAMPLE:

A bulb is connected to a circuit. The p.d. across the bulb is 250 V and the current through the bulb is 0.4 A.
Calculate how long it will take for 1 kJ of energy to be transferred to the bulb.

1) <u>Convert</u> the energy from kilojoules to joules.   1 kJ = 1000 J

2) Then <u>rearrange</u> $E = I \times V \times t$ for t. $t = \dfrac{E}{I \times V}$

3) <u>Substitute</u> into the rearranged equation $t = \dfrac{1000}{0.4 \times 250} = 10$ s

Energy is Transferred from Cells and Other Sources

1) Electrical appliances are designed to <u>transfer energy</u> to components in the circuit when a <u>current</u> flows.

Kettles transfer energy <u>electrically</u> from the mains a.c. supply to the <u>thermal</u> energy store of the heating element inside the kettle.

Energy is transferred <u>electrically</u> from the <u>battery</u> of a handheld fan to the <u>kinetic</u> energy store of the fan's motor.

2) Of course, <u>no</u> appliance transfers <u>all</u> energy completely usefully. The <u>higher</u> the <u>current</u>, the more energy is transferred to the <u>thermal</u> energy stores of the components (and then the surroundings).

3) This <u>heating</u> usually increases the <u>resistance</u> of the components, like you saw on page 95.

$I \times V \times t$ will give the total energy transferred to a component...

Be careful — the equation won't tell you how much of that energy is then <u>transferred usefully</u> by the component, or how much is <u>wasted</u>. To find that out, you need to know the component's <u>efficiency</u> (p.46).

Heating in Circuits and Power Ratings

Electrical devices are built to transfer energy. But nothing is perfect and some of this transferred energy ends up in thermal stores. This isn't always a bad thing though — devices like toasters and heaters make use of it.

Heating a Circuit isn't Always Bad

1) Heating up a component generally reduces its efficiency (p.46) — less energy is transferred to useful energy stores because more of it is being transferred to the thermal energy store of the component.

2) If the temperature gets too high, this can cause components in the circuit to melt — which means the circuit will stop working, or not work properly.

3) Fuses use this effect to protect circuits — they melt and break the circuit if the current gets too high (there's more on fuses on p.109).

4) The heating effect of an electric current can have other advantages. For example, it's ace if you want to heat something. Toasters contain a coil of wire with a really high resistance. When a current passes through the coil, its temperature increases so much that it glows and gives off infrared radiation. This radiation transfers energy to the bread and cooks it.

5) Filament bulbs and electric heaters work in a similar way.

Appliances Often Have a Power Rating

1) The total energy transferred by an appliance depends on how long the appliance is on for and its power.

2) The power of an appliance is the energy that it transfers per second. So the more energy it transfers in a given time, the higher its power. Power is measured in watts.

3) Appliances are often given a power rating — they're labelled with the maximum safe power that they can operate at. You can usually take this to be their maximum operating power.

4) The power rating tells you the maximum amount of energy transferred between stores per second when the appliance is in use.

> Microwaves have a range of power ratings. A microwave with a power rating of 500 W will take longer to cook food than one with a power rating of 750 W. This is because the 500 W microwave transfers less energy per second to the thermal energy store of the food, so it takes longer to cook.

5) This can help customers choose between models — the lower the power rating, the less electricity an appliance uses in a given time.

6) But, a higher power doesn't necessarily mean that it transfers more energy usefully. An appliance may be more powerful than another, but less efficient, meaning that it might still only transfer the same amount of energy (or even less) to useful stores (see p.45).

A higher power rating means more electricity is used per second...

The amount of electricity used by an appliance depends on its power rating and the amount of time it's switched on for. For example, the power rating of an electric lawn mower is typically about ten times higher than the power rating of a fridge (so the lawn mower will use more electricity per second), but a fridge probably uses more electricity in, for example, one year as it's always switched on.

Power in Circuits

Here come three equations for calculating electrical power, just for you. An equation for every occasion.

You can **Calculate** the **Power** of an Appliance

1) The power of an appliance can be found using:

> **Power (W) = Energy transferred (J) ÷ Time (s)**   or $P = \dfrac{E}{t}$

2) The power transferred by an appliance also depends on the potential difference (p.d.) across it, and the current flowing through it.

3) The p.d. tells you how much energy each unit of charge transfers (p.94), and the current tells you how much charge passes per unit time. So both will affect the rate that energy is transferred to an appliance, and the rate at which it transfers energy to other stores.

4) The power of an appliance can be found with:

> **Electrical power (W) = Current (A) × Potential difference (V)**   or $P = I \times V$

EXAMPLE:

A blender is connected to the mains electricity supply. In one minute, 20 700 J of energy is transferred to the blender. Calculate the power of the blender.

$P = E \div t = 20\ 700 \div 60 = 345\ W$

**The potential difference of the mains electricity supply is 230 V.
Calculate the current through the blender during this one minute period.**

1) Rearrange $P = I \times V$ for I. $I = P \div V$
2) Substitute into the rearranged equation. $I = 345 \div 230 = 1.5\ A$

You can also Calculate **Power** Using **Current** and **Resistance**

You can also find the power of an appliance if you don't know the potential difference. To do this, stick $V = I \times R$ from page 95 into $P = I \times V$, which gives you:

> $P = I^2 \times R$

Where P is the electrical power in watts (W), I is current in amperes (A) and R is the resistance in ohms (Ω).

EXAMPLE:

**A current of 5 A is passing through a motor, which has a resistance of 48 Ω.
Calculate the power of the motor.**

$P = I^2 \times R = 5^2 \times 48 = 1200\ W$

Make sure you use the right power equation...

If you're struggling to pick which power equation to use, it can be helpful to list the variables in the question, then decide which equation is suitable from the variables you've been given.

Warm-Up & Exam Questions

Put the brakes on — it's time to see what you can remember about energy and power in circuits.

Warm-Up Questions

1) State the equation relating energy transferred, current, potential difference and time.
2) Describe the main energy transfer that occurs in an electric toaster when it's plugged into the mains and turned on.
3) Name one appliance that makes use of the heating effect of an electric current.
4) Give the unit used to measure power.
5) Will a 60 W light bulb or a 40 W light bulb transfer more energy in a given amount of time?
6) State the equation that relates electrical power, current and resistance.

Exam Questions

1   **Figure 1** shows the power ratings for two kettles and the potential difference across each kettle.

	Power (kW)	Potential Difference (V)
Kettle A	2.8	230
Kettle B	3.0	230

Figure 1

   (a)   State the equation linking electrical power, current and potential difference.

[1 mark]

   (b)   Calculate the current drawn from the mains supply by kettle A.

[3 marks]

   (c)   A student is deciding whether to buy kettle A or kettle B.
         She wants to buy the kettle that boils water faster. Both kettles have the same efficiency.
         State and explain which kettle she should choose.

[2 marks]

2   A torch uses a 3.0 V power supply. A current of 0.5 A passes through a torch bulb.

   (a)   The torch is on for half an hour.
         Calculate the amount of energy transferred from the power supply in this time.
         Use the correct equation from the Physics Equation Sheet on the inside back cover.

[3 marks]

   (b)   The torch bulb is replaced. When the new torch bulb is connected
         to the 3.0 V power supply, 0.25 A of current passes through it.
         State how the power of the torch will be affected by this change.

[1 mark]

3   A single 1.5 V battery contains 13 000 J of energy in its chemical energy store.
    One of these batteries can be used to power a clock.
    A current of 0.2 mA passes through the clock when the battery is connected.

    Calculate how many batteries are needed to power the clock for 10 years.
    Use the correct equation from the Physics Equation Sheet on the inside back cover.

[3 marks]

Electricity in the Home

Now you've learnt the basics of <u>electrical circuits</u>, it's time to see how <u>electricity</u> is used in <u>everyday life</u>.

Mains Supply is **a.c.**, Battery Supply is **d.c.**

1) There are two types of electricity supplies — <u>alternating current</u> (a.c.) and <u>direct current</u> (d.c.).

2) In <u>a.c. supplies</u> the movement of the charges is <u>constantly</u> changing direction. <u>Alternating currents</u> are produced by <u>alternating voltages</u> (the <u>positive</u> and <u>negative</u> ends of the p.d. keep <u>alternating</u>).

3) The <u>UK mains supply</u> (the electricity in your home) is an a.c. supply at around <u>230 V</u>.

4) The frequency of the a.c. mains supply is <u>50 cycles per second</u> or <u>50 Hz</u> (hertz).

5) By contrast, cells and batteries supply <u>direct current</u> (d.c.).

6) In <u>direct current</u> the movement of the charges is only in one <u>direction</u>. It's created by a <u>direct voltage</u> (a p.d. that is <u>only positive</u> or <u>negative</u>, not both).

You can turn a.c. into d.c. by using a diode (p.97).

Most Cables Have **Three** Separate **Wires**

1) Most electrical appliances are connected to the mains supply by <u>three-core</u> cables. This means that they have <u>three wires</u> inside them, each with a <u>core of copper</u> and a <u>coloured plastic coating</u>.

2) The <u>colour</u> of the insulation on each cable shows its <u>purpose</u>.

3) The colours are <u>always</u> the <u>same</u> for <u>every</u> appliance. This is so that it is easy to tell the different wires <u>apart</u>.

<u>LIVE WIRE</u> — <u>brown</u>.
The live wire carries the voltage (potential difference, p.d.). It alternates between a <u>high +ve and −ve voltage</u> of about <u>230 V</u>.

<u>NEUTRAL WIRE</u> — <u>blue</u>.
The neutral wire <u>completes</u> the circuit — electricity normally flows <u>in</u> through the <u>live</u> wire and <u>out</u> through the <u>neutral</u> wire. The neutral wire is always at <u>0 V</u>.

<u>EARTH WIRE</u> — <u>green</u> and <u>yellow</u>.
The earth wire is for <u>safety</u> and <u>protecting</u> the <u>wiring</u>. It carries the current away if something goes <u>wrong</u> and stops the appliance casing becoming <u>live</u>. It's <u>also</u> at 0 V.

- The <u>p.d.</u> between the <u>live wire</u> and the <u>neutral wire</u> equals the <u>supply p.d.</u> (<u>230 V</u> for the mains).
- The <u>p.d.</u> between the <u>live wire</u> and the <u>earth wire</u> is also <u>230 V</u> for a mains-connected appliance.
- There is <u>no p.d.</u> between the <u>neutral wire</u> and the <u>earth wire</u> — they're both at 0 V.

4) <u>Plug sockets</u> have <u>switches</u> which are connected in the <u>live wire</u> of the circuit. This is so the circuit can be <u>broken</u> — the appliance becomes <u>isolated</u> and the risk of an <u>electric shock</u> is reduced.

5) <u>Fuses</u> and <u>circuit breakers</u> are also attached to the <u>live wire</u> in order to <u>isolate</u> the appliance if something goes wrong (p.109).

Mains electricity is always 230 V in the UK...

Make sure you can remember the <u>potential differences</u> between the three wires in mains wiring. Only the <u>live wire</u> has a potential difference that <u>isn't zero</u>, so there's a potential difference between the live wire and each of the other two wires (of 230 V). The potential difference between the earth and neutral wires is <u>zero</u>.

Electrical Safety

The <u>live wire</u> is capable of giving a dangerous <u>electric shock</u>, so safety precautions such as <u>fuses</u> are needed.

Touching the **Live Wire** Gives You an **Electric Shock**

1) Your <u>body</u> (just like the earth) is at <u>0 V</u>.

2) This means that if you touch the <u>live wire</u>, a <u>large potential difference</u> is produced across your body and a <u>current</u> flows through you.

3) This causes a large <u>electric shock</u> which could injure or even kill you.

4) Even if a plug socket is turned <u>off</u> (i.e. the switch is <u>open</u>) there is still a <u>danger</u> of an electric shock. A current <u>isn't flowing</u>, but there is still a p.d. in the live wire. If you made <u>contact</u> with the live wire, your body would provide a <u>link</u> between the supply and the earth, so a <u>current</u> would flow <u>through you</u>.

5) <u>Any</u> connection between <u>live</u> and <u>neutral</u> can be <u>dangerous</u>. If the link creates a <u>low resistance</u> path to earth, a huge current will flow, which could result in a fire.

Earthing and **Fuses** Prevent **Electrical Overloads**

1) <u>Surges</u> (sudden increases) in <u>current</u> can occur because of <u>changes in a circuit</u> (e.g. an appliance suddenly switching off) or because of a <u>fault</u> in an electrical <u>appliance</u>.

2) Current surges can lead to the <u>circuits and wiring</u> in your appliances <u>melting</u> or causing a <u>fire</u>, and <u>faulty</u> appliances can cause deadly <u>electric shocks</u>.

3) The <u>earth wire</u> and a <u>fuse</u> are included in electrical appliances to prevent this from happening. The example below shows how they work:

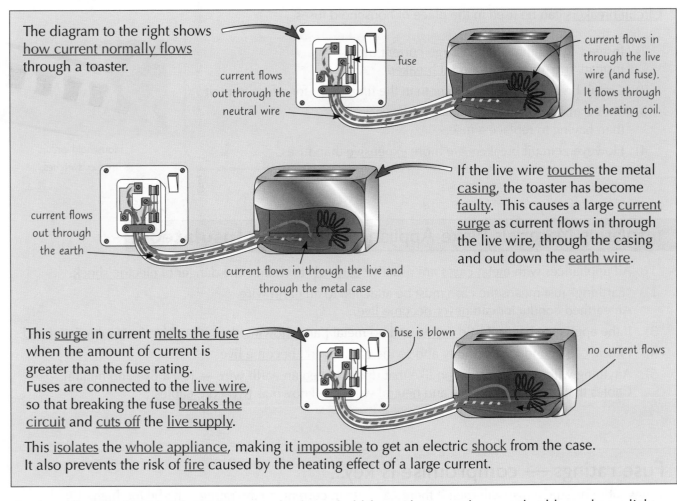

The diagram to the right shows <u>how current normally flows</u> through a toaster.

current flows out through the neutral wire

fuse

current flows in through the live wire (and fuse). It flows through the heating coil.

current flows out through the earth

current flows in through the live and through the metal case

If the live wire <u>touches</u> the metal <u>casing</u>, the toaster has become <u>faulty</u>. This causes a large <u>current surge</u> as current flows in through the live wire, through the casing and out down the <u>earth wire</u>.

This <u>surge</u> in current <u>melts the fuse</u> when the amount of current is greater than the fuse rating. Fuses are connected to the <u>live wire</u>, so that breaking the fuse <u>breaks the circuit</u> and <u>cuts off</u> the <u>live supply</u>.

fuse is blown

no current flows

This <u>isolates</u> the <u>whole appliance</u>, making it <u>impossible</u> to get an electric <u>shock</u> from the case. It also prevents the risk of <u>fire</u> caused by the heating effect of a large current.

4) As well as the fuses in plugs, there are also <u>household fuses</u> (these are the ones that blow when a light bulb goes). These work in the <u>same way</u>, but protect the <u>wiring in the house</u>, not just in an appliance.

Section 6 — Electricity and Circuits

Electrical Safety

Fuses and circuit breakers are super important. And questions on them cover a whole barrel of fun — electrical current, resistance, potential difference... Read this page and make sure you've got it sussed.

A **Fuse Rating** is the **Minimum Current** needed to **Break** a Fuse

1) Fuses should be rated as near as possible but just higher than the normal operating current.

2) The larger the current, the thicker the cable you need to carry it (to stop the cable getting too hot and melting). That's why the fuse rating needed for cables usually increases with cable thickness.

EXAMPLE:

A 1 kW hair dryer is connected to a 230 V supply.
Suggest whether a 3 A, a 5 A or a 13 A fuse is needed.

1) Convert from kilowatts to watts.   1 kW = 1000 W

2) Then rearrange $P = I \times V$ (p.106) for I. $I = P \div V$

3) Substitute into the rearranged equation. $I = 1000 \div 230 = 4.3... A$

4) Choose the fuse with the rating just higher than the calculated current.   So a 5 A fuse is needed.

Circuit Breakers are Even **Safer** Than **Fuses**

Circuit breakers can be used in the place of household fuses.

1) Instead of melting a fuse, a large current may instead 'trip' (turn off) a circuit breaker.

2) Circuit breakers turn off quicker than the time taken for a fuse to melt.

3) They can also be reset, which is much easier than having to replace a fuse.

4) However, circuit breakers are more expensive than fuses.

Household circuit breaker switches.

Insulating Materials Make Appliances **"Double Insulated"**

1) All appliances with metal cases are usually "earthed" to reduce the danger of electric shock.

2) "Earthing" just means the case must be attached to an earth wire. An earthed conductor can never become live.

3) If the appliance has a plastic casing and no metal parts showing then it's said to be double insulated.

4) Plastic can't conduct electricity and so the casing can't become live.

5) Anything with double insulation like that doesn't need an earth wire — just a live and neutral. Cables that only carry the live and neutral wires are known as two-core cables.

Fuse ratings — compromise is key...

You want to be sure a fuse will melt if there's a surge in current, so the rating can't be too high. On the other hand you don't want it to be so low that it will blow whilst the appliance is functioning safely.

Warm-Up & Exam Questions

Time to see if you've been paying close attention to the last three pages — have a go at these delightful warm-up and exam questions. If you get any wrong, look back for a quick recap.

Warm-Up Questions

1) Is the electricity supplied by a battery alternating current or direct current?
2) Explain the function of the neutral wire in mains wiring.
3) What is the p.d. between the live wire and the neutral wire in mains wiring?
4) Which wire should a fuse be fitted to in mains wiring?
5) True or false? It is best to use a fuse with a rating that is much lower than the appliance's normal operating current.

Exam Questions

1   Appliances with a metal casing are usually connected to the mains using a three-core cable.

   (a)   Mains electricity provides alternating current.
       State what is meant by alternating current.

[1 mark]

Figure 1

   (b)   **Figure 1** shows an electrical cable that has become frayed so that the metal part of the live wire is exposed. Explain why you would get an electric shock if you touched the exposed wire.

[3 marks]

2   A kettle is connected to the mains electricity supply.

The kettle develops a fault so that the live wire is in contact with the kettle's metal casing, causing it to become live.

   (a)   Explain how the earth wire and the fuse isolate the kettle in this situation.

[3 marks]

   (b)   Give an alternative to using a fuse to isolate a faulty appliance.

[1 mark]

   (c)   An appliance has a casing that is made entirely from plastic, and has no metal parts showing. Explain why the appliance does not need an earth wire.

[1 mark]

Revision Summary for Section 6

Well that's all for <u>Section 6</u> folks — try out these revision summary questions to see how much you've learnt.

*   Try these questions and <u>tick off each one</u> when you <u>get it right</u>.
*   When you've done <u>all the questions</u> for a subtopic and are <u>completely happy</u> with it, tick off the topic.

Circuit Basics (p.93-98) ☑

1) Draw the circuit symbols for: a cell, a filament lamp, a diode, a motor and an LDR.   ☑
2) What is meant by the potential difference in a circuit?   ☑
3) What is meant by the resistance of a circuit?   ☑
4) Define current and state an equation that links charge, current and time, with units for each.   ☑
5) What is the equation that links potential difference, current and resistance?   ☑
6) Describe how the resistance of a fixed resistor varies with temperature.   ☑
7) True or false? To measure the current through a component, an ammeter must be connected in parallel with the component.   ☑
8) Explain how you would investigate how the current through a component affects its resistance.   ☑
9) Sketch the *I-V* graph for a diode.   ☑
10) Describe how the resistance of an LDR varies with light intensity.   ☑
11) Give one everyday use of an LDR.   ☑

Series and Parallel Circuits (p.100-102) ☑

12) True or false? Potential difference is shared between components in a series circuit.   ☑
13) True or false? Adding resistors in series increases the total resistance of the circuit.   ☑
14) Give one difference between series and parallel circuits.   ☑
15) Does adding two resistors in parallel increase or decrease the total resistance of a circuit?   ☑

Power and Energy Transfers in Circuits (p.104-106) ☑

16) Give two disadvantages of the heating effect in an electrical circuit.   ☑
17) What is a power rating?   ☑
18) State the equation that links power, energy transferred and time.   ☑

Electricity in the Home and Electrical Safety (p.108-110) ☑

19) True or false? Mains supply electricity is an alternating current.   ☑
20) What is the frequency of the UK mains supply?   ☑
21) Give the potential difference between the live wire and the earth wire in mains wiring.   ☑
22) Which wire is connected to the metal casing of an appliance in order to make the appliance safe to use?   ☑
23) True or false? Circuit breakers must be replaced each time they 'trip'.   ☑

Magnets and Magnetic Fields

Magnetic fields are produced by magnets, and can be shown with field lines. Well that was easy.

Magnets Produce **Magnetic Fields**

1) All magnets have two poles — north and south.

2) All magnets produce a magnetic field — a region where other magnets or magnetic materials (see next page) experience a force.

3) You can show a magnetic field by drawing magnetic field lines.

4) The lines always go from north to south and they show which way a force would act on a north pole at that point in the field.

5) The closer together the lines are, the stronger the magnetic field.

6) The further away from a magnet you get, the weaker the field is.

7) The magnetic field is strongest at the poles of a magnet. This means that magnetic forces are also strongest at the poles.

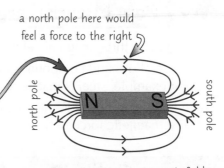

a north pole here would feel a force to the right

north pole   south pole

To see the shape of a magnetic field, place a piece of card over a magnet and sprinkle iron filings onto it. The filings line up with the field lines — but they won't show you the direction of the field.

Magnetic Fields Cause **Forces** between **Magnets**

1) Between two magnets there is a magnetic force that can be attractive or repulsive. Two poles that are the same (these are called like poles) will repel each other. Two unlike poles will attract each other.

2) Placing the north and south poles of two bar magnets near each other creates a uniform field between the two poles. The magnetic field is the same strength everywhere between the poles.

3) If you're asked to draw a uniform magnetic field, you need to draw at least three field lines, parallel to each other and all the same distance apart.

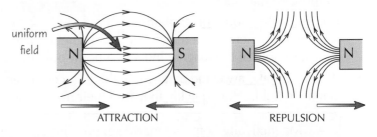

uniform field

ATTRACTION   REPULSION

Don't forget the arrows on your field lines.

Plotting Compasses Show the **Directions** of Magnetic Fields

1) Inside a compass is a tiny bar magnet called a needle. A compass needle always lines up with the magnetic field it's in.

2) You can use a compass to build up a picture of what the field around a magnet looks like:

- Put the magnet on a piece of paper and draw round it.

- Place the compass on the paper near the magnet. The needle will point in the direction of the field line at this position.

- Mark the direction of the compass needle by drawing two dots — one at each end of the needle.

- Then move the compass so that the tail end of the needle is where the tip of the needle was in the previous position and put a dot by the tip of the needle. Repeat this and then join up the marks you've made — you'll end up with a drawing of one field line around the magnet.

- Repeat this method at different points around the magnet to get several field lines. Make sure you draw arrows from north to south on your field lines.

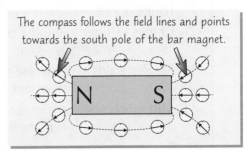

The compass follows the field lines and points towards the south pole of the bar magnet.

3) When they're not near a magnet, compasses always point towards the Earth's North Pole. This is because the Earth generates its own magnetic field (and the North Pole is actually a magnetic south pole). This shows the inside (core) of the Earth must be magnetic.

Permanent and Induced Magnets

Magnetic fields don't just affect <u>magnets</u> — they affect a few special <u>magnetic materials</u> too.

Very Few Materials are Magnetic

1) The main <u>three</u> magnetic elements are <u>iron</u>, <u>nickel</u> and <u>cobalt</u>.

2) Some alloys and compounds of these metals are also magnetic.
For example, <u>steel</u> is magnetic because it contains <u>iron</u>.

3) If you put a magnetic material near a magnet, it is <u>attracted</u> to that magnet.
The magnetic force between a magnet and a magnetic material is <u>always</u> attractive.

Magnets Can be Permanent or Induced

1) <u>Permanent</u> magnets (e.g. bar magnets) produce their own magnetic field <u>all the time</u>.

2) <u>Induced</u> (or <u>temporary</u>) magnets only produce a magnetic field while they're <u>in</u> another <u>magnetic field</u>.

3) If you put any <u>magnetic material</u> into a magnetic field, it becomes an <u>induced</u> magnet.

4) This <u>magnetic induction</u> explains why the force between a magnet and a magnetic material is always <u>attractive</u> — the south pole of the magnet induces a north pole in the material, and vice versa.

5) When you <u>take away</u> the magnetic field, induced magnets return to normal and <u>stop producing</u> a magnetic field. How <u>quickly</u> they lose their magnetism depends on the material they're made from.

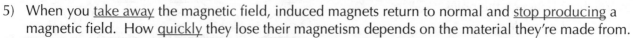

The <u>magnetic material</u> becomes <u>magnetised</u> when it is brought near the <u>bar magnet</u>. It has its own <u>poles</u> and <u>magnetic field</u>:

induced poles

- Magnetically '<u>soft</u>' materials, e.g. pure <u>iron</u> and <u>nickel-iron alloys</u>, lose their magnetism very quickly.
- Magnetically '<u>hard</u>' materials, e.g. <u>steel</u>, lose their magnetism more slowly. <u>Permanent magnets</u> are made from magnetically hard materials.

Magnetic Materials have Lots of Uses

There are many different <u>uses</u> of <u>magnetic materials</u>, the number of which has grown since the invention of <u>electromagnets</u> (p.117). For example:

1) <u>Fridge doors</u> — there is a <u>permanent</u> magnetic strip in your fridge door to keep it closed.

2) <u>Cranes</u> — these use <u>induced</u> electromagnets to <u>attract</u> and <u>move</u> magnetic materials — e.g. moving <u>scrap metal</u> in scrap yards.

3) <u>Maglev trains</u> — these use <u>magnetic repulsion</u> to make trains <u>float</u> slightly above the track (to reduce losses from <u>friction</u>) and to <u>propel</u> them along.

4) <u>MRI machines</u> — these use magnetic fields to create <u>images</u> of the inside of your body without having to use <u>ionising radiation</u> (like X-rays, p.67).

5) <u>Speakers and microphones</u> — these use magnets to <u>create</u> or <u>detect</u> vibrations.

Magnets attract magnetic materials due to magnetic induction...

However, once the permanent magnet is <u>removed</u>, the <u>induced magnet</u> becomes <u>unmagnetised</u> again.

Electromagnetism and The Motor Effect

A <u>magnetic field</u> can be produced by a <u>current passing through a wire</u>. This can result in something called the <u>motor effect</u> if the current-carrying <u>wire</u> is placed in an <u>external magnetic field</u> (e.g. of a bar magnet).

A **Moving Charge** Creates a Magnetic Field

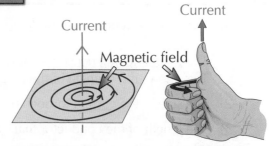

1) When a <u>current flows</u> through a <u>long, straight conductor</u> (e.g. a <u>wire</u>) a <u>magnetic field</u> is created <u>around</u> it.

2) The field is made up of <u>concentric circles</u> perpendicular to the wire, with the wire in the centre.

3) Changing the <u>direction</u> of the <u>current</u> changes the direction of the <u>magnetic field</u> — use the <u>right-hand thumb rule</u> to work out which way it goes.

4) In experiments, you can use a <u>plotting compass</u> to find its direction (see p.113).

5) The <u>larger</u> the current through the wire, or the <u>closer</u> to the wire you are, the <u>stronger</u> the field is.

> <u>The Right-Hand Thumb Rule</u>
> Using your right hand, point your <u>thumb</u> in the direction of <u>current</u> and <u>curl</u> your fingers. The direction of your <u>fingers</u> is the direction of the <u>field</u>.

A **Current** in a **Magnetic Field** Experiences a **Force**

1) When a <u>current-carrying conductor</u> (e.g. a <u>wire</u>) is put between magnetic poles, the two <u>magnetic fields</u> interact. The result is a <u>force</u> on the wire. This is known as the <u>motor effect</u>.

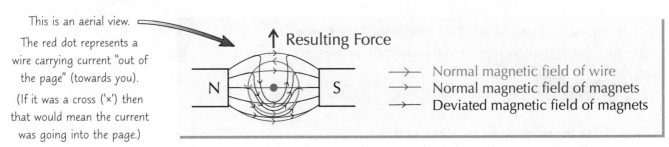

This is an aerial view.

The red dot represents a wire carrying current "out of the page" (towards you).

(If it was a cross ('×') then that would mean the current was going into the page.)

↑ Resulting Force

→ Normal magnetic field of wire
→ Normal magnetic field of magnets
→ Deviated magnetic field of magnets

2) To experience the <u>full force</u>, the <u>wire</u> has to be at <u>90°</u> (right angles) to the <u>magnetic field</u>. If the wire runs <u>along</u> the <u>magnetic field</u>, it won't experience <u>any force at all</u>. At angles in between, it'll feel <u>some</u> force.

3) The force always acts in the <u>same direction</u> relative to the <u>magnetic field</u> and the <u>direction of the current</u> in the wire. So changing the <u>direction</u> of either the <u>magnetic field</u> or the <u>current</u> will change the direction of the <u>force</u>.

The wire also exerts an equal and opposite force on the magnet (from Newton's Third Law, see p.26) but we're just looking at the force on the wire.

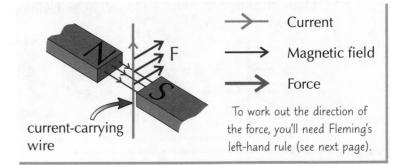

current-carrying wire

→ Current

→ Magnetic field

→ Force

To work out the direction of the force, you'll need Fleming's left-hand rule (see next page).

Just point your thumb in the direction of the current...

... and your <u>fingers</u> show the <u>direction of the field</u> it produces. Remember, it's always your <u>right thumb</u>. Not your left. You'll use your left hand on the next page though, so it shouldn't feel left out...

The Motor Effect

So you know that a <u>current-carrying wire</u> experiences a <u>force</u> in a <u>magnetic field</u>.
Time now to see how to find the <u>size</u> and the <u>direction</u> of this force.

You Can Find the **Size** of the **Force**...

The size of the <u>force</u> acting on a <u>conductor</u> in a <u>magnetic field</u> depends on three things:

1) The <u>magnetic flux density</u> — how many <u>field</u> (<u>flux</u>) lines there are in a <u>region</u>.
   This shows the <u>strength</u> of the magnetic field (p.113).

2) The size of the <u>current</u> through the conductor.

3) The <u>length</u> of the conductor that's <u>in</u> the magnetic field.

When the current is at <u>90°</u> to the magnetic field it is in, the <u>force</u> acting on it can be found using the equation:

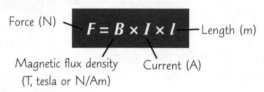

Force (N) — $F = B \times I \times l$ — Length (m)

Magnetic flux density   Current (A)
(T, tesla or N/Am)

... and **Which Way** it's Acting

You can find the direction of the force on a current-carrying
conductor with <u>Fleming's left-hand rule</u>.

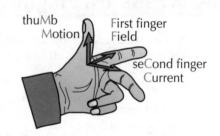

thuMb — Motion
First finger — Field
seCond finger — Current

1) Using your <u>left hand</u>, point your <u>First finger</u>
   in the direction of the magnetic <u>Field</u>.

2) Point your <u>seCond</u> finger in the direction of the <u>Current</u>.

3) Your <u>thuMb</u> will then point in the direction of the <u>force</u> (<u>M</u>otion).

EXAMPLE:

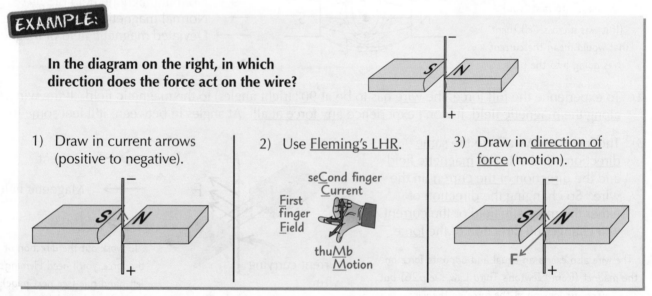

**In the diagram on the right, in which
direction does the force act on the wire?**

1) Draw in current arrows
   (positive to negative).

2) Use <u>Fleming's LHR</u>.

seCond finger
Current
First
finger
Field
thuMb
Motion

3) Draw in <u>direction of
   force</u> (motion).

F

Fleming's left-hand rule can really come in handy...

EXAM TIP

Use the left-hand rule in the exam. You might look a bit silly, but it makes getting those marks so
much easier. So don't get tripped up — your <u>First finger</u> corresponds to the direction of the <u>Field</u>,
your <u>seCond finger</u> points in the direction of the <u>Current</u>, and finally your <u>thuMb</u> points in the
direction of the force (or <u>Motion</u>). If you can remember that, then those marks will come easily.

Solenoids

A <u>solenoid</u> is a fancy way of saying <u>coils of wire</u> with a <u>current</u> flowing through them. The current means that solenoids produce a <u>magnetic field</u> which, as it turns out, is <u>similar</u> to the <u>field</u> around a <u>bar magnet</u>.

A **Solenoid** is a **Long Coil** of Wire

1) Around a <u>single loop</u> of current-carrying wire, the magnetic field looks like this:

2) You can <u>increase</u> the <u>strength</u> of the magnetic field produced by a length of wire by <u>wrapping</u> it into a <u>long coil</u> with <u>lots</u> of loops, called a <u>solenoid</u>.

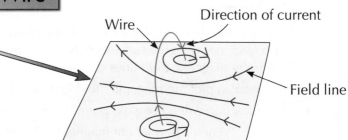

3) The <u>field lines</u> around each separate loop of wire <u>line up</u>.

- <u>Inside</u> the solenoid, you get <u>lots</u> of field lines <u>pointing in the same direction</u>. The magnetic field is <u>strong</u> and almost <u>uniform</u>.

- <u>Outside</u> the coil, the <u>overlapping</u> field lines <u>cancel each other out</u> — so the field is <u>weak</u> apart from at the <u>ends</u> of the solenoid.

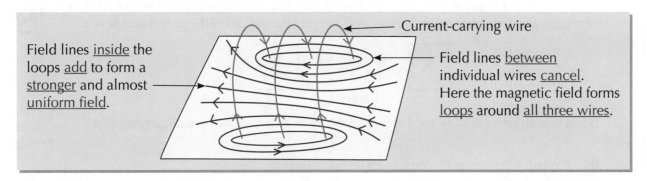

Field lines <u>inside</u> the loops <u>add</u> to form a <u>stronger</u> and almost <u>uniform field</u>.

Current-carrying wire

Field lines <u>between</u> individual wires <u>cancel</u>. Here the magnetic field forms <u>loops</u> around <u>all three wires</u>.

4) You end up with a field that looks like the one around a <u>bar magnet</u>. The <u>direction</u> of the field depends on the <u>direction of the current</u> (p.115).

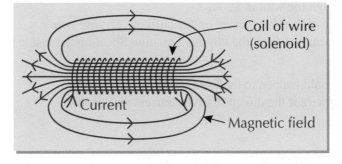

Coil of wire (solenoid)

Current

Magnetic field

5) A <u>solenoid</u> is an <u>example</u> of an <u>ELECTROMAGNET</u> — a magnet with a magnetic field that can be turned <u>on</u> and <u>off</u> using an <u>electric current</u>.

6) You can <u>increase</u> the field strength of the solenoid <u>even more</u> by putting a block of <u>iron</u> in the <u>centre</u> of the coil. This <u>iron core</u> becomes an <u>induced magnet</u> (see p.114) whenever current is flowing.

The fields around bar magnets and solenoids are the same shape...

The main <u>advantage</u> of using an <u>electromagnet</u> (such as a <u>solenoid</u>) rather than a bar magnet is that the <u>magnetic field</u> can be <u>turned on</u> and <u>off</u> with the <u>current</u>. This makes an electromagnet pretty <u>handy</u>.

Warm-Up & Exam Questions

It's time for another page of questions to see how much you've absorbed. If you can do the warm-up questions without breaking into a sweat, then see how you get on with the exam questions below.

Warm-Up Questions

1) a) State whether there will be a force of attraction, repulsion, or no force between the two magnets on the right.
   b) Sketch the magnetic field lines occurring between the two bar magnets.

2) Describe how to plot the magnetic field lines of a bar magnet using a compass.

3) In which direction will a compass point if it is not near any magnets?

4) True or false? When a permanent magnet is placed next to a magnetic material, the magnetic material becomes an induced magnet that repels the permanent magnet.

Exam Questions

1 **Figure 1** shows an aerial view of a current-carrying wire in a magnetic field generated by two bar magnets. The circle represents the wire carrying current out of the page, towards you.

N   ○   S

Figure 1

   (a) Draw an arrow to show the direction of the force acting on the current-carrying wire.

   [1 mark]

   (b) Explain what causes the force to act on the current-carrying wire.

   [1 mark]

   (c) The magnetic field strength of the field generated by the bar magnets is 0.028 T.
   7.0 cm of the current-carrying wire lies within the magnetic field of the bar magnets.
   The current through the wire is 5.5 A.
   Calculate the size of the force acting on the current-carrying wire.
   Use the correct equation from the Physics Equation Sheet on the inside back cover.

   [2 marks]

   (d) Describe what would happen to the force acting on the current-carrying wire if the direction of the current was reversed.

   [1 mark]

2 A student makes an electromagnet by wrapping a current-carrying wire into a solenoid around a nail. When the nail is brought close to some paperclips, the paperclips are attracted to the nail.

   (a) Explain why a strong uniform field is created within the coils of the solenoid.

   [2 marks]

   (b) Suggest an element that the nail might contain.

   [1 mark]

   (c) The student wants to increase the magnetic field strength of the electromagnet.
   State **one** way in which he could do this.

   [1 mark]

Electromagnetic Induction

Electromagnetic induction — sounds scary, but read this page carefully and it shouldn't be too complicated.

A **Changing** Magnetic Field Induces a **Potential Difference** in a **Wire**

> Electromagnetic Induction: The induction of a potential difference (and current if there's a complete circuit) in a wire which is experiencing a change in magnetic field.

Induces is a fancy word for creates.

1) There are two different situations where you get electromagnetic induction. The first is if an electrical conductor (e.g. a coil of wire) and a magnetic field move relative to each other:

- You can do this by moving/rotating either a magnet in a coil of wire OR a conductor (wire) in a magnetic field (the conductor "cuts through" the magnetic field lines).

- If you move or rotate the magnet (or conductor) in the opposite direction, then the potential difference/current will be reversed. Likewise if the polarity of the magnet is reversed (by turning the magnet around), then the potential difference/current will be reversed too.

- If you keep the magnet (or the coil) moving backwards and forwards, or keep it rotating in the same direction, you produce an alternating current (p.108).

Voltmeter

2) You also get an induced p.d. when the magnetic field through an electrical conductor changes (gets bigger or smaller or reverses). This is what happens in a transformer (p.120).

3) You can increase the size of the induced p.d. by increasing the STRENGTH of the magnetic field, increasing the SPEED of movement/change of field or having MORE TURNS PER UNIT LENGTH on the coil of wire.

Induced Current **Opposes** the Change that Made It

1) So, a change in magnetic field can induce a current in a wire. But, as you saw on page 115, when a current flows through a wire, a magnetic field is created around the wire. (Yep, that's a second magnetic field — different to the one whose field lines were being cut in the first place.)

2) The magnetic field created by an induced current always acts against the change that made it (whether that's the movement of a wire or a change in the field it's in). Basically, it's trying to return things to the way they were.

3) This means that the induced current always opposes the change that made it.

Electromagnetic induction works whether the coil or the field moves

Electromagnetic induction may seem like a difficult concept to grasp, but there are really only a couple of key things to remember. It doesn't matter what's moving, electromagnetic induction occurs as long as field lines are being 'cut'. And the current that's induced will oppose the change that generated it.

Transformers and The National Grid

Transformers are an application of electromagnetic induction for you to sink your teeth into.

Transformers Change the p.d. — but Only for Alternating Current

1) Transformers use induction to change the size of the potential difference of an alternating current.
2) They all have two coils of wire, the primary and the secondary coils, joined with an iron core.
3) When an alternating p.d. is applied across the primary coil, it produces an alternating magnetic field.
4) The iron in the core is a magnetic material (see p.114) that is easily magnetised and demagnetised. Because the coil is producing an alternating magnetic field, the magnetisation in the core also alternates.
5) This changing magnetic field induces a p.d. in the secondary coil.

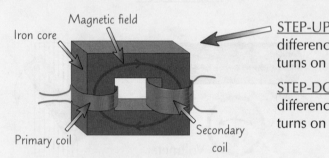

STEP-UP TRANSFORMERS step the potential difference up (i.e. increase it). They have more turns on the secondary coil than the primary coil.

STEP-DOWN TRANSFORMERS step the potential difference down (i.e. decrease it). They have more turns on the primary coil than the secondary.

6) Transformers are almost 100% efficient.
7) So you can assume that the input power is equal to the output power.
8) Using $P = I \times V$ (page 106), you can write this as:

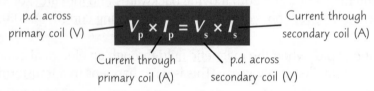

$$V_p \times I_p = V_s \times I_s$$

p.d. across primary coil (V)

Current through primary coil (A)

Current through secondary coil (A)

p.d. across secondary coil (V)

9) $V_p \times I_p$ is the power input at the primary coil. $V_s \times I_s$ is the power output at the secondary coil.

Transformers are Used in The National Grid

1) Once electricity has been generated in a power station, it goes into the national grid — a network of wires and transformers that connects UK power stations to consumers (anyone who uses electricity).
2) The national grid has to transfer loads of energy each second, which means it transmits electricity at a high power (as power = energy transferred ÷ time taken, $P = E ÷ t$, p.106).
3) Electrical power = current × potential difference ($P = I \times V$, p.106), so to transmit the huge amounts of power needed, you either need a high potential difference or a high current.
4) But a high current makes wires heat up, so loads of energy is wasted to thermal energy stores.
5) So to reduce these losses and make the national grid more efficient, high-potential difference, low-resistance cables, and transformers are used.
6) Step-up transformers at power stations boost the p.d. up really high (400 000 V) and keep the current low. Step-down transformers then bring it back down to safe, usable levels at the consumers' end.

The national grid — it's a powerful thing...

Electricity is transmitted across the national grid with a high p.d. in order to transmit large amounts of power. It's also transmitted at a low current to reduce energy losses by heating. To get this high p.d. and low current, a step-up transformer is used to transfer the electricity from the power station to the national grid.

Warm-Up & Exam Questions

There were lots of new ideas in that section, not to mention that equation on page 120. Better have a go at these questions so you can really see what's gone in and what you might need to go over again.

Warm-Up Questions

1) What is meant by electromagnetic induction?
2) True or false? An induced current will always oppose the change that made it.
3) Do step-up transformers have more turns on their primary or secondary coil?
4) Why is a high current not used to transmit large amounts of power across the national grid?

Exam Questions

1   **Figure 1** shows a coil of wire connected to a voltmeter. A student moves a bar magnet into the coil as shown. The pointer on the voltmeter moves to the left.

(a)   Explain why the pointer moves.

[1 mark]

(b)   State how the student could get the voltmeter's pointer to move to the right.

[1 mark]

(c)   State how he could get a larger reading on the voltmeter.

[1 mark]

(d)   State what reading the voltmeter will show if the student holds the magnet still inside the coil.

[1 mark]

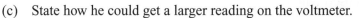

Figure 1

2   The national grid supplies consumers across the UK with electricity from power stations.

(a)   Describe what step-up and step-down transformers are used for in the national grid.

[2 marks]

Figure 2 shows the structure of a transformer.

(b)   Explain how an alternating current in the primary coil causes an alternating p.d. to occur in the secondary coil.

[3 marks]

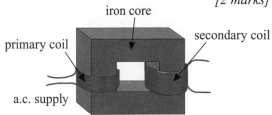

Figure 2

3   A student tests a transformer by connecting a power supply with an alternating current of 2.5 A and a potential difference of 12 V to the primary coil. The potential difference across the secondary coil is 4 V.

Calculate the current in the secondary coil, I_S.

[2 marks]

Revision Summary for Section 7

Congratulations — you've battled to the end of <u>Section 7</u>. Now see how much you've learnt.
*   Try these questions and <u>tick off each one</u> when you <u>get it right</u>.
*   When you've done <u>all the questions</u> under a heading and are <u>completely happy</u>, tick it off.

Magnetism (p.113-114) ☑

1) What is a magnetic field? In which direction do magnetic field lines point? ☑
2) Sketch the magnetic field lines around a bar magnet. ☑
3) Explain why a plotting compass points north when it is far away from a magnet. ☑
4) Give three examples of magnetic materials. ☑
5) What is the difference between a permanent magnet and an induced magnet? ☑

Electromagnetism and the Motor Effect (p.115-117) ☑

6) Describe the magnetic field around a current-carrying wire. ☑
7) What is Fleming's left-hand rule? ☑
8) Name two ways you could decrease the force on a current-carrying wire in a magnetic field. ☑
9) What is meant by an electromagnet? ☑

Electromagnetic Induction and Transformers (p.119-120) ☑

10) Describe how you can induce a current in a coil of wire. ☑
11) Give two ways you could reverse the direction of an induced current. ☑
12) What kind of current are transformers used with? ☑
13) True or false? Step-down transformers have more coils on their primary coil
    than on their secondary. ☑
14) A transformer has an input p.d. of 100 V and an output p.d. of 20 V. What kind of transformer is it? ☑
15) Explain how transformers are used to improve efficiency when transmitting electricity across the
    national grid. ☑

Density

Density tells you how much <u>mass</u> is packed into a given <u>volume</u> of space. You need to be able to work it out, as well as carry out <u>practicals</u> to work out the densities of liquids and solids. Lucky you.

Density is the **Mass per Unit Volume** of a Substance

Density is a measure of the '<u>compactness</u>' of a substance. It relates the <u>mass</u> of a substance to how much <u>space</u> it takes up (i.e. it's a substance's <u>mass</u> per <u>unit volume</u>).

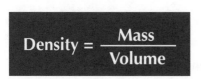

$$\text{Density} = \frac{\text{Mass}}{\text{Volume}}$$

The symbol for density is a Greek letter rho (ρ) — it looks like a p but it isn't.

1) The <u>units</u> of <u>density</u> can be <u>kg/m³</u> (where the <u>mass</u> is in <u>kg</u> and the <u>volume</u> is in <u>m³</u>) or <u>g/cm³</u> (where the mass is in g and the volume is in <u>cm³</u>). $1 \text{ g/cm}^3 = 1000 \text{ kg/m}^3$.

2) The <u>density</u> of an <u>object</u> depends on what it's <u>made of</u>. Density <u>doesn't vary</u> with <u>size</u> or <u>shape</u>.

3) The average <u>density</u> of an object determines whether it <u>floats</u> or <u>sinks</u> — a solid object will <u>float</u> on a fluid if it has a <u>lower average density</u> than the fluid.

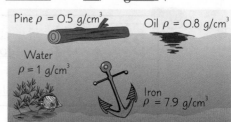

Pine $\rho = 0.5$ g/cm³   Oil $\rho = 0.8$ g/cm³

Water $\rho = 1$ g/cm³

Iron $\rho = 7.9$ g/cm³

You Need to be Able to **Measure Density** in **Different Ways**

To Find the Density of a Liquid

PRACTICAL

1) Place a <u>measuring cylinder</u> on a balance and <u>zero</u> the balance (see p.137).

2) Pour <u>10 ml</u> of the liquid into the measuring cylinder and record the liquid's <u>mass</u>.

3) Pour <u>another 10 ml</u> into the measuring cylinder and record the <u>total volume</u> and <u>mass</u>. Repeat this process until the measuring cylinder is <u>full</u>.

4) For each measurement, use the <u>formula</u> to find the <u>density</u>. (Remember that 1 ml = 1 cm³.)

5) Finally, take an <u>average</u> of your calculated densities to get an accurate value for the <u>density</u> of the <u>liquid</u>.

To Find the Density of a Solid Object

PRACTICAL

1) Use a <u>balance</u> to measure its <u>mass</u> (see p.137).

2) For some solid shapes, you can find the <u>volume</u> using a <u>formula</u>. E.g. the volume of a cube is just width × height × length.

Make sure you know the formulas for the volumes of basic shapes.

3) For a trickier shaped-solid, you can find its volume by <u>submerging</u> it in a <u>eureka can</u> filled with water. The water <u>displaced</u> by the object will be <u>transferred</u> to the <u>measuring cylinder</u>:

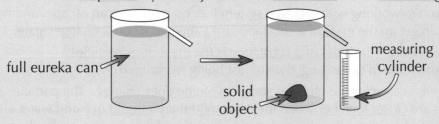

full eureka can   measuring cylinder

solid object

4) Record the <u>volume</u> of water in the measuring cylinder. This is the <u>volume</u> of the <u>object</u>.

5) Plug the object's <u>mass</u> and <u>volume</u> into the <u>formula</u> above to find its <u>density</u>.

Kinetic Theory and States of Matter

You've definitely met a lot of the terms on this page before, but that <u>doesn't</u> mean you can skip it...

Kinetic Theory is a Way of Explaining Matter

1) In kinetic theory, you can think of the particles that make up matter as <u>tiny balls</u>.

2) You can explain the ways that matter behaves in terms of how these balls <u>move</u>, and the <u>forces</u> between them. For example, kinetic theory is used to describe the <u>states of matter</u>.

Matter Can Be In Different States

1) <u>Three states of matter</u> are <u>solid</u> (e.g. ice), <u>liquid</u> (e.g. water) and <u>gas</u> (e.g. water vapour).

2) The <u>particles</u> of a substance in each state are <u>the same</u>
   — only the <u>arrangement</u> and <u>energy</u> of the particles are <u>different</u>.

Solids

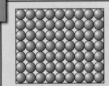

1) <u>Strong forces</u> of attraction hold the particles <u>close together</u> in a <u>fixed</u>, <u>regular</u> arrangement.

2) The particles don't have much <u>energy</u> in their <u>kinetic energy stores</u> so they can only <u>vibrate</u> about their <u>fixed</u> positions.

Liquids

1) The forces of attraction between the particles are <u>weaker</u>.

2) The particles are <u>close together</u>, but can <u>move past each other</u> and form <u>irregular</u> arrangements.

3) They have <u>more energy</u> in their <u>kinetic energy stores</u> than the particles in a <u>solid</u> — they move in <u>random directions</u> at <u>low speeds</u>.

Gases

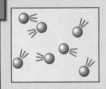

1) There are <u>almost no</u> forces of attraction between the particles.

2) For any given substance, in the gas state its particles will have <u>more energy</u> than in the solid state or the liquid state.

3) They are <u>free to move</u>, and travel in <u>random directions</u> and at <u>high speeds</u>.

You Need to Know the Changes of State

The energy transfers that take place during a change in state are covered on p.130.

1) You need to know the names of the different <u>changes of state</u>:
   - <u>melting</u> — solid to liquid
   - <u>condensing</u> — gas to liquid
   - <u>sublimating</u> — solid to gas
   - <u>freezing</u> — liquid to solid
   - <u>evaporating/boiling</u> — liquid to gas

2) If you <u>reverse</u> a change of state, the particles <u>go back</u> to how they were before.

3) So changes of state are <u>physical changes</u> (only the <u>form</u> of a substance changes).
   These are <u>different</u> from <u>chemical reactions</u>, where <u>new substances</u> are created by the reaction.

   1) Provided you're working with a <u>closed system</u> (i.e. no particles can escape, and no new particles can get in) the <u>mass</u> of a substance <u>isn't affected</u> when it changes <u>state</u>.

   2) This makes sense — the <u>mass of a substance</u> is the <u>mass of its particles</u>, and the particles aren't changing, they're just being rearranged.

   3) However, when a substance changes state its <u>volume does change</u>. The particles in most substances are <u>closer together</u> when they're a <u>solid</u> than a <u>liquid</u> (ice and water are an exception), and are closer together when they're a <u>liquid</u> than a <u>gas</u> (see the diagrams above).

   4) Since <u>density = mass ÷ volume</u> (p.123), then density must change too. Generally, substances are <u>most dense</u> when they're <u>solids</u> and <u>least dense</u> when they're <u>gases</u>.

Internal Energy and Absolute Zero

According to kinetic theory, everything is made of tiny little particles.
The energy of a system is determined by the energy of the particles that make it up.

Internal Energy is Stored by the Particles That Make Up a System

1) The particles in a system vibrate or move around — they have energy in their kinetic energy stores. The more energy they have in their kinetic energy stores, the faster the particles move.

2) They also have energy in their potential energy stores due to their positions. Usually, the further apart they are from each other, the more energy the particles have in this store.

3) The energy stored in a system is stored by its particles.

4) The internal energy of a system is the total energy that its particles have in their kinetic and potential energy stores.

5) The energy in the thermal energy store of a system is the energy in just the kinetic energy stores of its particles.

6) Heating a system transfers energy to its particles, so heating a system always increases its internal energy.

7) This leads to a change in temperature (when energy is transferred to the kinetic energy stores of the particles) or a change in state (when energy is transferred to the potential energy stores of the particles — see p.130).

Absolute Zero is as Cold as Stuff Can Get — 0 kelvin

1) If you increase the temperature of something, you give its particles more energy — they move about more quickly or vibrate more. In the same way, if you cool a substance down, you're reducing the energy of the particles.

2) In theory, the coldest that anything can ever get is -273 °C — this temperature is known as absolute zero.

3) At absolute zero, the particles have as little energy in their kinetic stores as it's possible to get — they're pretty much still.

4) Absolute zero is the start of the Kelvin scale of temperature.

5) A temperature change of 1 °C is also a change of 1 kelvin. The two scales are pretty similar — the only difference is where the zero occurs.

6) To convert from degrees Celsius to kelvins, just add 273.

7) And to convert from kelvins to degrees Celsius, just subtract 273.

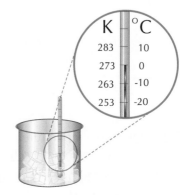

You can't get colder than absolute zero...

Always double check that your answer seems sensible in the exam. For example, nothing can get colder than 0 K or – 273 °C, so if your answer is below that, you've done something wrong in your calculations.

Gas Pressure

Kinetic theory helps explain how temperature, pressure and the energy in kinetic energy stores are all related.

The **Average Speed** of Particles **Increases** With **Temperature**

1) According to kinetic theory, the particles in a gas are constantly moving with random directions and speeds (see p.124).

2) If you increase the temperature of a gas, you transfer energy into the kinetic energy stores of its particles.

3) So as you increase the temperature of a gas, the average speed of its particles increases. This is because the energy in the particles' kinetic energy stores is $\frac{1}{2} \times m \times v^2$ — p.41.

Colliding Gas Particles Create **Pressure**

1) Particles in a gas hardly take up any space. Most of the gas is empty space.
2) As gas particles move about at high speeds, they bang into each other and whatever else happens to get in the way. When they collide with something, they exert a force on it.
3) In a sealed container, the outward gas pressure is the total force exerted by all of the particles in the gas on a unit area of the container walls.

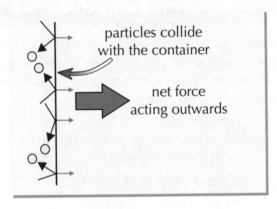

particles collide with the container

net force acting outwards

A sealed container is an example of a closed system — no matter can get in or out.

4) The higher the temperature of the gas, the faster the particles move and the more often they collide with the container.
5) The force exerted by each particle during a collision also increases as the temperature increases.
6) So increasing the temperature of a fixed volume of gas increases its pressure.

The higher the temperature, the greater the pressure...

Imagine throwing a tennis ball at a wall. The faster you throw the tennis ball, the greater the force (and pressure) it exerts on the wall. It's the same idea with gases — when you increase the temperature of a gas, the particles move faster and create a greater pressure on the container walls.

Warm-Up and Exam Questions

Time to try your hand at some questions, before getting to grips with the rest of the section.

Warm-Up Questions

1) What is density a measure of?
2) In what state can the particles in a substance move in random directions at high speeds?
3) Name the change of state for a solid changing into a gas.
4) Are changes of state chemical or physical changes?
5) How does cooling a system affect its internal energy?
6) State the temperature of absolute zero in degrees Celsius.
7) If a gas is kept at a constant volume, explain why increasing the temperature of the gas causes the gas pressure to increase.

Exam Questions

1   A block of lead is solid at room temperature. **Grade 4-6**

   (a)   Describe the arrangement and movement of the particles in a solid.

   [2 marks]

   (b)   The lead block has a mass of 850.5 g and a volume of 75.0 cm³.
         Calculate the density of the lead block. Give your answer in g/cm³.

   [2 marks]

   (c)   If the lead block is heated to 327.5 °C, it can change from a solid to a liquid.
         Give the name of this process.

   [1 mark]

PRACTICAL

2   A student has a collection of metal toy soldiers each made from the same metal.
    Each toy soldier has a different volume.

   (a)   Which of the following statements about the toy soldiers is true?

   ☐ **A**   The masses and densities of each of the toy soldiers are the same.

   ☐ **B**   The masses of each of the toy soldiers are the same, but their densities will vary.

   ☐ **C**   The densities of each of the toy soldiers are the same, but their masses will vary.

   ☐ **D**   The densities and masses of each toy soldier will vary.

   [1 mark]

   (b)   The student wants to measure the density of one of the toy soldiers.
         He has a eureka can (a beaker with a spout in the side, as shown in
         Figure 1), a measuring cylinder, a mass balance and some water.
         State the **two** quantities the student must measure
         in order to calculate the density of the toy soldier.

   [2 marks]

   Figure 1

   *(c)   Describe the steps the student could take to find the density
         of the toy soldier using the equipment he has.

   [6 marks]

Specific Heat Capacity and Specific Latent Heat

Specific heat capacity is really just a sciencey way of saying how hard it is to heat something up, and specific latent heat is a measure of how much energy is needed to change the state of a substance.

Specific Heat Capacity Relates Temperature and Energy

1) It takes more energy to increase the temperature of some materials than others.

2) For example, you need 4200 J to warm 1 kg of water by 1 °C, but only 139 J to warm 1 kg of mercury by 1 °C.

3) Materials that need to gain lots of energy to warm up also release loads of energy when they cool down again. They store a lot of energy for a given change in temperature.

4) The change in the energy stored in a substance when you heat it is related to the change in its temperature by its specific heat capacity.

5) The specific heat capacity of a substance is the change in energy in the substance's thermal energy store needed to raise the temperature of 1 kg of that substance by 1 °C.

6) You need to know how to use the equation relating energy, mass, specific heat capacity and temperature.

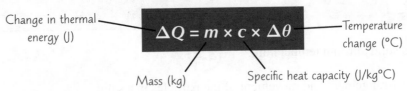

Change in thermal energy (J) ⟶ $\Delta Q = m \times c \times \Delta\theta$ ⟵ Temperature change (°C)

Mass (kg)   Specific heat capacity (J/kg°C)

7) The Δs in the equation just mean 'change in'.

Specific Latent Heat is the Energy Needed to Change State

1) The specific latent heat (SLH) of a change of state of a substance is the amount of energy needed to change 1 kg of it from one state to another without changing its temperature.

2) For cooling, specific latent heat is the energy released by a change in state.

3) Specific latent heat is different for different materials, and for changing between different states.

4) The specific latent heat for changing between a solid and a liquid (melting or freezing) is called the specific latent heat of fusion. The specific latent heat for changing between a liquid and a gas (evaporating, boiling or condensing) is called the specific latent heat of vaporisation.

5) You can work out the energy needed (or released) when a substance of mass m changes state using this formula:

Thermal energy (J) = Mass (kg) × Specific Latent Heat (J/kg)

$$\frac{Q}{m \times L}$$

EXAMPLE: The specific latent heat of vaporisation for water (boiling) is 2 260 000 J/kg. How much energy is needed to completely boil 1.50 kg of water at 100 °C?

1) Just plug the numbers into the formula. $Q = m \times L$
$= 1.50 \times 2\,260\,000$

2) The units are joules because it's energy. $= 3\,390\,000$ J

Don't get these two mixed up...

Specific heat capacity is to do with changes in temperature, but specific latent heat is to do with changing state (which occurs without a change in temperature). They have similar names, but they're not the same.

Investigating Water

It's time to cover another of those <u>core practicals</u> — and it's all about investigating... <u>water</u>.
Okay, so it doesn't sound that fun, but you have to be able to find out the <u>specific heat capacity</u> of water.

You can Find the **Specific Heat Capacity** of Water

You can use the experiment below to find the <u>specific heat capacity</u> of <u>water</u> — or any <u>liquid</u>
for that matter. In the experiment, an <u>electric immersion heater</u> is used to heat a container full
of water. It is <u>assumed</u> that <u>all</u> of the energy transferred to the heater from its power supply
is transferred <u>usefully</u> to the water — i.e. all of the energy transferred heats the water.

1) First, place your container on a <u>mass balance</u>.

2) <u>Zero</u> the balance and fill the container with water. Record the <u>mass</u> of the water.

3) Set up the experiment as shown — make sure the joulemeter reads
<u>zero</u> and place a <u>lid</u> on the container if you have one.

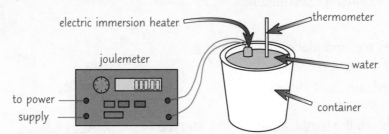

You can use this set up
with solid blocks to find
the SHC of solids.

4) Measure the <u>temperature</u> of the water, then turn on the power.

5) Keep an eye on the <u>thermometer</u>. When the temperature has increased by e.g. <u>ten degrees</u>,
stop the experiment and record the <u>energy</u> on the joulemeter, and the <u>increase in temperature</u>.

6) You can then calculate the specific heat capacity of the
water by <u>rearranging</u> $\Delta Q = m \times c \times \Delta\theta$ to give you
$c = \Delta Q \div (m \times \Delta\theta)$ and plugging in your measurements.

Alternatively, you could also use a
voltmeter and ammeter instead of
a joulemeter, time how long the
heater was on for, then calculate
the energy supplied (p.104).

7) <u>Repeat</u> the whole experiment at least three times,
then calculate an <u>average</u> of the specific heat capacity (p.9).

Use **Thermal Insulation** to get More **Accurate** Results

1) During <u>any</u> process, some energy is always <u>wasted</u>.

2) So in the experiment above, not <u>all</u> of the energy transferred from the power supply
is used to heat the water (although we assume it's true to make calculations easier).

3) Some is <u>lost</u> heating up the wires of the immersion heater and some
is transferred by heating to the container and the air around it.

4) To <u>reduce</u> these <u>unwanted energy transfers</u> and make your result more <u>accurate</u>
(p.7), you should wrap the container in a <u>thermally insulating</u> material
(e.g. cotton wool) and place it on an <u>insulating surface</u>, like a cork mat.

5) <u>Thermal insulators</u> reduce the <u>rate</u> at which energy is transferred by <u>heating</u>,
which means that <u>less energy</u> is transferred to the thermal energy stores of
the surroundings. There's more about thermal insulation on page 47.

Think about how you could improve your experiments...

In this practical, wrapping the container in a <u>thermal insulator</u> is a great example of a way in
which a method can be improved. In all experiments you need to be able to <u>evaluate</u> the method
used and <u>suggest improvements</u> that could be made to make the results <u>more accurate</u>.

Investigating Water

And now it's time to <u>investigate</u> what happens to the <u>temperature</u> of water during a <u>change of state</u>.

You Need to **Put In Energy** to **Break Intermolecular Bonds**

1) When a system is <u>heated</u> and its <u>state changes</u> (e.g. melting, boiling), <u>energy</u> is <u>transferred</u> to the <u>potential energy stores</u> of the particles instead of to their kinetic energy stores.

2) The <u>particles</u> in the system <u>move apart</u> from each other and the <u>intermolecular forces</u> between the particles get <u>weaker</u> (see p.124).

3) Because the amount of energy in the particles' <u>kinetic energy stores</u> stays the <u>same</u>, the <u>average speed</u> of the particles and the <u>temperature</u> of the system remain <u>constant</u> whilst the substance <u>changes state</u>.

4) During a change of state due to <u>cooling</u>, the particles <u>lose energy</u> from their <u>potential energy stores</u>. They move <u>closer together</u> and the <u>intermolecular forces</u> between them get <u>stronger</u>. Their <u>average speed</u> still doesn't change though (so the <u>temperature</u> still remains <u>constant</u>).

5) You can see this by doing this simple <u>experiment</u>:

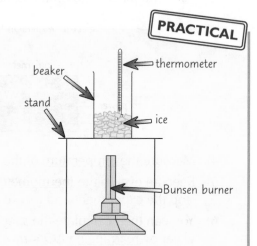

PRACTICAL

1) Fill a <u>beaker</u> with <u>crushed ice</u>, and place a <u>thermometer</u> into the beaker to record the <u>temperature</u> of the ice.

2) Start a stopwatch and <u>gradually heat</u> the beaker full of ice using a Bunsen burner.

3) Every twenty seconds, record the <u>temperature</u> and the <u>current state</u> of the ice (e.g. partially melted, completely melted).

4) Continue this process until all of the ice has turned into water and the water begins to <u>boil</u>.

5) <u>Stop</u> the stopwatch and <u>turn off</u> the Bunsen burner.

6) Plot a graph of <u>temperature against time</u> for your experiment.

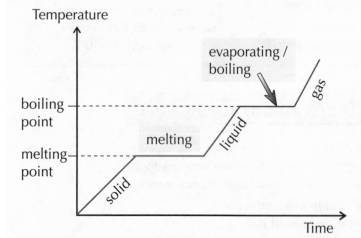

7) You should get a graph similar to the <u>blue</u> sections in the graph on the left.

8) The <u>purple line</u> shows what your graph would look like if you were able to trap and <u>heat</u> the <u>water vapour</u> produced.

9) Comparing the graph to your measurements, you should see that the <u>flat spots</u> occur when there is a <u>change of state</u>.

10) Energy is being transferred to the <u>potential</u> energy stores of the water particles at these points, so the temperature <u>doesn't change</u>.

11) If you carried out an experiment for <u>cooling water</u> instead of heating it, you would get a <u>similar</u> graph. However, the <u>temperature-time</u> graph for a substance <u>cooled</u> from a gas has a <u>negative</u> gradient and <u>flat spots</u> where the substance is condensing or freezing.

The temperature of a substance is constant as it changes state...

Energy isn't transferred to the particles' kinetic energy stores for a <u>change of state</u>, so the <u>temperature</u> of the substance stays the <u>same</u> and you get <u>flat spots</u> on a temperature-time graph. Learn that, and understand it.

Warm-Up & Exam Questions

Time to test yourself on specific heat capacity and specific latent heat. There's no escaping it, get going.

Warm-Up Questions

1) What is the specific heat capacity of a material?
2) What are the units of specific latent heat?
3) In an experiment to find the specific heat capacity of water, a container of water is wrapped in a thermally insulating material and heated. Explain how this improves the results of the experiment.
4) Sketch a temperature-time graph for water turning into ice.

Exam Questions

1   47 100 J of energy is required to convert 40.8 g of liquid methanol to gaseous methanol without changing its temperature.

    Calculate the specific latent heat of vaporisation of methanol. Give your answer in J/kg.
    Use the correct equation from the Physics Equation Sheet on the inside back cover.

    [2 marks]

2   36 000 J of energy is transferred to a 0.5 kg concrete block.
    The block increases in temperature from 20 °C to 100 °C.

    (a)   Calculate the specific heat capacity of the concrete block.
          Use the correct equation from the Physics Equation Sheet on the inside back cover.

    [2 marks]

    (b)   **Figure 1** shows a storage heater in a room. Energy is transferred to the thermal energy store of the electric storage heater at night, and then transferred away to the thermal energy stores of the surroundings during the day. Lead has a specific heat capacity of 126 J/kg°C.

          Using your answer to (a), explain why concrete blocks are used in storage heaters rather than lead blocks.

    [3 marks]

Figure 1

PRACTICAL

3   A student uses an electrical immersion heater to transfer energy to a beaker containing 1.0 kg of water.
    She produces a graph of the energy supplied against the increase in temperature of the water, shown in **Figure 2**.

    (a)   Use the gradient of the line of best fit in **Figure 2** to determine a value for the specific heat capacity of water in J/kg°C.

    [3 marks]

    (b)   State and explain whether you would you expect the true value for the specific heat capacity of water to be higher or lower than the value found in this experiment.

    [2 marks]

Figure 2

Section 8 — Matter

Elasticity

Forces don't just make objects <u>move</u>, they can also make them <u>change shape</u>. Whether they change shape <u>temporarily</u> or <u>permanently</u> depends on <u>the object</u> and the forces applied.

Stretching, Compressing or Bending Transfers Energy

1) When you apply a force to an object you may cause it to <u>bend</u>, <u>compress</u> or <u>stretch</u>.

2) To do this, you need <u>more than one</u> force acting on the object — otherwise the object would simply <u>move</u> in the direction of the <u>applied force</u>, instead of changing shape.

3) <u>Work is done</u> when a force stretches or compresses an object and causes energy to be transferred to the <u>elastic potential energy</u> store of the object.

4) If it is <u>elastically distorted</u> (see below), <u>ALL</u> this energy is transferred to the object's <u>elastic potential energy store</u> (see p.41).

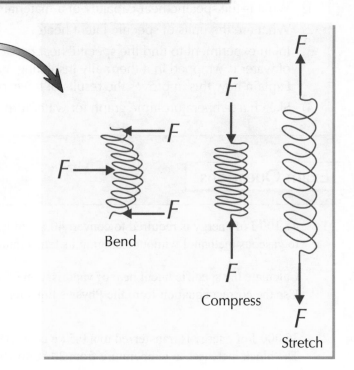

Bend

Compress

Stretch

Elastic Distortion

1) An object has been <u>elastically distorted</u> if it can <u>go back</u> to its <u>original shape</u> and <u>length</u> after the force has been removed.

2) Objects that can be elastically distorted are called <u>elastic objects</u> (e.g. a spring).

Inelastic Distortion

1) An object has been <u>inelastically distorted</u> if it <u>doesn't</u> return to its <u>original shape</u> and <u>length</u> after the force has been removed.

2) The <u>elastic limit</u> is the point where an object <u>stops</u> distorting <u>elastically</u> and <u>begins</u> to distort <u>inelastically</u>.

Elastic objects are only elastic up to a certain point...

Remember the difference between <u>elastic distortion</u> and <u>inelastic distortion</u>. If an <u>object</u> has been <u>elastically distorted</u>, it will <u>return</u> to its <u>original shape</u> when you <u>remove the force</u>. If it's been <u>inelastically distorted</u>, its shape will have been <u>changed permanently</u> — for example, an over-stretched spring will stay stretched even after you remove the force.

Elasticity

Springs obey a really handy little equation that relates the force on them to their extension — for a while at least. Thankfully, you can plot a graph to see where this equation is valid.

Extension is Directly Proportional to Force...

If a spring is supported at the top and a weight is attached to the bottom, it stretches.

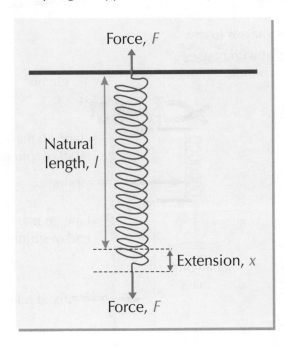

1) The extension of a stretched spring (or certain other elastic objects) is directly proportional to the load or force applied — so $F \propto x$.

2) This means that there is a linear relationship between force and extension. (If you plotted a force-extension graph for the spring, it would be a straight line.)

3) This is the equation:

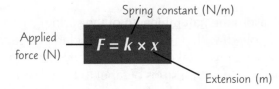

Spring constant (N/m)

Applied force (N)

$$F = k \times x$$

Extension (m)

4) For a linear relationship, the gradient of an object's force-extension graph is equal to its spring constant.

5) The spring constant, depends on the material that you are stretching — a stiffer spring has a greater spring constant.

6) The equation also works for compression (where x is just the difference between the natural and compressed lengths — the compression).

...But this Stops Working when the Force is Great Enough

There's a limit to the amount of force you can apply to an object for the extension to keep on increasing proportionally.

1) The graph shows force against extension for an elastic object.

2) There is a maximum force above which the graph curves, showing that extension is no longer proportional to force.

3) The relationship is now non-linear — the object stretches more for each unit increase in force. This point is known as the limit of proportionality and is shown on the graph at the point marked P.

4) The elastic limit (see previous page) is marked as E. Past this point, the object is permanently stretched.

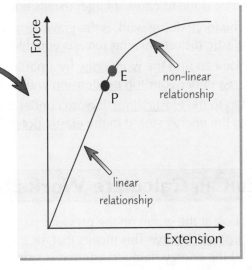

EXAM TIP

The spring constant is measured in N/m...

Be careful with units when doing calculations with springs. Some exam questions might have the extension in centimetres, but the spring constant is measured in newtons per metre. So convert the extension into metres before you do any calculations, or you'll get the wrong answer.

Investigating Elasticity

You can do an easy experiment to see exactly how adding masses to a spring causes it to stretch.

You Can **Investigate** the Link Between **Extension and Work Done**

Set up the apparatus as shown in the diagram. Make sure you have plenty of extra masses, then measure the mass of each (with a mass balance) and calculate its weight (the force applied) using $W = m \times g$ (p.30).

You could do a quick pilot experiment first to find out what size masses to use.

- Using an identical spring to the one you will be testing, load it with masses one at a time and record the force (weight) and extension each time.

- Plot a force-extension graph and check that you get a nice straight line for at least the first 6 points. If it curves too early, you need to use smaller masses.

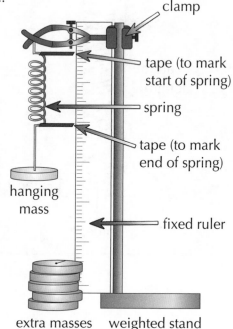

1) Measure the natural length of the spring (when no load is applied) with a millimetre ruler clamped to the stand. Make sure you take the reading at eye level and add markers (e.g. thin strips of tape) to the top and bottom of the spring to make the reading more accurate.

2) Add a mass to the spring and allow the spring to come to rest. Record the mass and measure the new length of the spring. The extension is the change in length.

3) Repeat this process until you have enough measurements (no fewer than 6).

4) Plot a force-extension graph of your results. It will only start to curve if you exceed the limit of proportionality, but don't worry if yours doesn't (as long as you've got the straight line bit).

1) You should find that a larger force causes a bigger extension.

2) You can also think of this as more work needing to be done to cause a larger extension.

3) The force doing work is the gravitational force and for linear elastic distortions, this force is equal to $F = k \times x$.

4) You can find the work done by a particular force by calculating the area under your force-extension graph up to that value of force.

5) Up to the elastic limit, the area under the graph (work done) is also equal to the energy stored in the elastic potential energy store (see below).

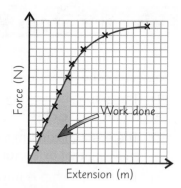

You Can **Calculate Work Done** for **Linear** Relationships

1) Look at the graph on the previous page. The elastic limit is always at or beyond the limit of proportionality. This means that for a linear relationship, the distortion is always elastic — all the energy being transferred is stored in the spring's elastic potential energy store.

2) For a linear relationship, the energy in the elastic potential energy store (and so the work done) can be found using:

$$E = \tfrac{1}{2} \times k \times x^2$$

Energy transferred in stretching (J) — Spring constant (N/m) — Extension² (m²)

Warm-Up & Exam Questions

Time to do some work and stretch yourself with these questions.

Warm-Up Questions

1) True or false? You can stretch a spring by only applying one force to it.
2) What is meant by elastic distortion?
3) State the formula linking force, spring constant and extension.

Exam Questions

PRACTICAL

1   A student investigates the relationship between
the force applied to a spring and its extension.

Figure 1 shows the force-extension graph of his results.

Calculate the work done to stretch the spring by 4 cm.

[2 marks]

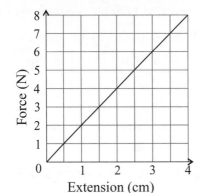

Figure 1

PRACTICAL

2   A teacher shows his students an experiment to show how a spring extends when masses
are hung from it. He hangs a number of 90 g masses from a 50 g hook attached to
the base of the spring. He records the extension of the spring and the total weight
of the masses and hook each time he adds a mass to the bottom of the spring.

(a) Give the independent variable in this experiment

[1 mark]

(b) Give **one** control variable in this experiment.

[1 mark]

(c) When a force of 4 N is applied to the spring, the spring extends elastically by 2.5 cm.
Calculate the spring constant of the spring.

[3 marks]

(d) The teacher applies a 15 N force to the spring. When he removes the force, the spring is 7 cm long.
The original length of the spring was 5 cm. Describe what has happened to the spring.

[1 mark]

3   A spring is compressed linearly and elastically. It takes 36 J of energy to compress the spring.
The original length of the spring is 1.20 m. The spring has a spring constant of 400 N/m.
Calculate the length of the spring after it has been compressed.
Use the correct equation from the Physics Equation Sheet on the inside back cover.

[3 marks]

Revision Summary for Section 8

Phew, that's the end of <u>Section 8</u> — the last one in the book. Test yourself before you celebrate.
- Try these questions and <u>tick off each one</u> when you <u>get it right</u>.
- When you've done <u>all the questions</u> under a heading and are <u>completely happy</u> with it, tick it off.

Density and the Kinetic Theory of Matter (p.123-130) ☑

1) What is the formula for density? What are the units of density?
2) Briefly describe an experiment to find the density of a liquid.
3) For each state of matter, describe the arrangement of the particles.
4) Name five changes of state.
5) True or false? Mass stays the same when a substance changes state.
6) What is absolute zero? What value does it have in kelvin?
7) Describe how a gas exerts a pressure on the walls of its container.
8) What happens to the pressure of a gas in a sealed container of fixed volume when it is heated?
9) What are the units of specific heat capacity?
10) Define specific latent heat.
11) Describe an experiment that could be used to plot a temperature-time graph
     for ice melting into water.

Stretching, Compressing and Bending (p.132-134) ☑

12) Explain why you need more than one force acting on an object to cause it to stretch.
13) What is the difference between an elastic and an inelastic distortion?
14) How do you find the spring constant from a linear force-extension graph?
15) Draw a typical force-extension graph for an elastic object being stretched past its elastic limit.
16) Describe an experiment that could be used to investigate the relationship between the
     applied force on a spring and the extension of the spring.

Apparatus and Techniques

This section covers <u>practical skills</u> you'll need to know about for your course.

- You'll have to do <u>7 core practicals</u> (experiments) for physics. These are covered earlier in the book and they're <u>highlighted</u> with <u>practical stamps</u> like this one.
- The following pages of this section cover some <u>extra bits and bobs</u> you need to know about practical work. First up, using apparatus to take measurements...

Mass Should Be Measured Using a Balance

1) For a <u>solid</u>, set the balance to <u>zero</u> and then place your object onto the scale and read off the mass.

2) If you're measuring the mass of a <u>liquid</u>, start by putting an empty <u>container</u> onto the <u>balance</u>. Next, <u>reset</u> the balance to zero.

3) Then just pour your <u>liquid</u> into the container and record the mass displayed.

Measure Most Lengths with a Ruler

1) In most cases a bog-standard <u>centimetre ruler</u> can be used to measure <u>length</u>. It depends on what you're measuring though — <u>metre rulers</u> or long <u>measuring tapes</u> are handy for <u>large</u> distances, while <u>micrometers</u> are used for measuring tiny things like the <u>diameter of a wire</u>.

2) The ruler should always be <u>parallel to</u> what you want to measure.

3) If you're dealing with something where it's <u>tricky</u> to measure just <u>one</u> accurately (e.g. water ripples, p.57), you can measure the length of <u>some</u> of them and then <u>divide</u> to find the <u>length of one</u>.

4) If you're taking <u>multiple measurements</u> of the <u>same</u> object (e.g. to measure changes in length) then make sure you always measure from the <u>same point</u> on the object. It can help to draw or stick a small <u>marker</u> onto the object, and <u>line it up</u> with the ruler so that the measurement is always read from the marker.

5) Make sure the ruler and the object are always at <u>eye level</u> when you take a reading. This stops <u>parallax</u> affecting your results, e.g. if you're investigating the link between <u>force</u> and the <u>extension</u> of a spring (p.134).

<u>Parallax</u> is where a measurement appears to <u>change</u> based on <u>where you're looking from</u>.

The <u>blue line</u> is the measurement taken when the spring is at <u>eye level</u>. It shows the correct length of the spring.

If the eye <u>isn't level</u> with this line, it looks like the spring is <u>too long</u> or <u>too short</u>.

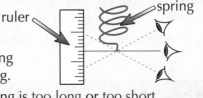

Use a Protractor to Find Angles

1) First align the <u>vertex</u> (point) of the angle with the mark in the <u>centre</u> of the protractor.

2) Line up the <u>base line</u> of the protractor with one line that forms the <u>angle</u> and then measure the angle of the other line using the scale on the <u>protractor</u>.

3) If the lines creating the angle are very <u>thick</u>, align the protractor and measure the angle from the <u>centre</u> of the lines. Using a <u>sharp pencil</u> to trace light rays or draw diagrams helps to <u>reduce errors</u> when measuring angles.

4) If the lines are <u>too short</u> to measure easily, you may have to <u>extend</u> them. Again, make sure you use a <u>sharp pencil</u> to do this.

Apparatus and Techniques

Measure **Temperature** Accurately with a **Thermometer**

1) Make sure the <u>bulb</u> of your thermometer is <u>completely submerged</u> in any substance you're measuring the temperature of.

2) Wait for the temperature reading to <u>stabilise</u> before you take your initial reading.

3) Again, read your measurement off the <u>scale</u> on a thermometer at <u>eye level</u>.

bulb

Measuring Cylinders and **Pipettes** Measure **Liquid Volumes**

1) <u>Measuring cylinders</u> are the most common way to measure a liquid.

2) They come in all different <u>sizes</u>. Make sure you choose one that's the <u>right size</u> for the measurement you want to make. It's no good using a huge 1 dm³ cylinder to measure out 2 cm³ of a liquid — the graduations (markings for scale) will be <u>too big</u> and you'll end up with <u>massive errors</u>. It'd be much better to use one that measures up to 10 cm³.

3) You can also use a <u>pipette</u> to measure volume. <u>Pipettes</u> are used to suck up and <u>transfer</u> volumes of liquid between containers.

4) <u>Graduated pipettes</u> are used to transfer accurate volumes. A <u>pipette filler</u> is attached to the end of a graduated pipette to <u>control</u> the amount of liquid being drawn up.

5) Whichever method you use, always read the volume from the <u>bottom of the meniscus</u> (the curved upper surface of the liquid) when it's at <u>eye level</u>.

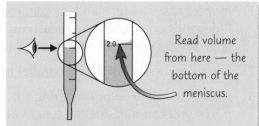
2.0
Read volume from here — the bottom of the meniscus.

You May Have to Measure the **Time Taken** for a Change

1) You should use a <u>stopwatch</u> to <u>time</u> most experiments — they're more <u>accurate</u> than regular watches.

2) Always make sure you <u>start</u> and <u>stop</u> the stopwatch at exactly the right time. Or alternatively, set an <u>alarm</u> on the stopwatch so you know exactly when to stop an experiment or take a reading.

3) You might be able to use a <u>light gate</u> instead (see below). This will <u>reduce the errors</u> in your experiment.

Light Gates Measure **Speed** and **Acceleration**

1) A <u>light gate</u> sends a <u>beam</u> of light (or sometimes infrared) from one side of the gate to a <u>detector</u> on the other side. When something passes through the gate, the beam of light is <u>interrupted</u>. The light gate then measures <u>how long</u> the beam was undetected for.

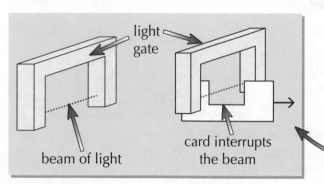
light gate
card interrupts the beam
beam of light

Have a look at page 28 for an example of a light gate being used.

2) To find the <u>speed</u> of an object, connect the light gate to a <u>computer</u>. Measure the <u>length</u> of the object and <u>input</u> this using the software. It will then <u>automatically calculate</u> the speed of the object as it passes through the beam.

3) To measure <u>acceleration</u>, use an object that interrupts the signal <u>twice</u> in a <u>short</u> period of time, e.g. a piece of card with a gap cut into the middle.

4) The light gate measures the speed for each section of the object and uses this to calculate its <u>acceleration</u>. This can then be read from the <u>computer screen</u>.

Working With Electronics

Electrical devices are used in a bunch of experiments, so make sure you know how to use them.

You Have to Interpret Circuit Diagrams

Before you get cracking on an experiment involving any kind of electrical devices, you have to plan and build your circuit using a circuit diagram. Make sure you know all of the circuit symbols on page 93 so you're not stumped before you've even started.

You Can Measure Potential Difference and Current

Voltmeters Measure Potential Difference

1) If you're using an analogue voltmeter, choose the voltmeter with the most appropriate unit (e.g. V or mV).

2) If you're using a digital voltmeter, you'll most likely be able to switch between them.

3) Connect the voltmeter in parallel (p.101) across the component you want to test.

4) The wires that come with a voltmeter are usually red (positive) and black (negative). These go into the red and black coloured ports on the voltmeter.

5) Then simply read the potential difference from the scale (or from the screen if it's digital).

Ammeters Measure Current

1) Just like with voltmeters, choose the ammeter with the most appropriate unit.

2) Connect the ammeter in series (p.100) with the component you want to test, making sure they're both on the same branch. Again, they usually have red and black ports to show you where to connect your wires.

3) Read off the current shown on the scale or by the screen.

Turn your circuit off between readings to prevent wires overheating and affecting your results (p.95).

Multimeters Measure Both

1) Instead of having a separate ammeter and voltmeter, many circuits use multimeters. These are devices that measure a range of properties — usually potential difference, current and resistance.

2) If you want to find potential difference, make sure the red wire is plugged into the port that has a 'V' (for volts).

3) To find the current, use the port labelled 'A' or 'mA' (for amps).

4) The dial on the multimeter should then be turned to the relevant section, e.g. to 'A' to measure current in amps. The screen will display the value you're measuring.

Don't get your wires in a tangle when you're using circuits...

When you're dealing with voltmeters, ammeters and multimeters, you need to make sure that you wire them into your circuit correctly, otherwise you could mess up your readings. Just remember, the red wires should go into the red ports and the black wires should go into the black ports.

Safety Precautions

There's <u>danger</u> all around, particularly in science experiments. But don't let this put you off. Just be aware of the <u>hazards</u> and take <u>sensible precautions</u>. Read on to find out more...

Be **Careful** When You Do Experiments

1) There are always hazards in any experiment, so <u>before</u> you start an experiment you should read and follow any <u>safety precautions</u> to do with your method or the apparatus you're using.

2) Stop masses and equipment falling by using <u>clamp stands</u>.

3) Make sure any masses you're using in investigations are of a <u>sensible weight</u> so they don't break the equipment they're used with. Also, make sure strings used in <u>pulley systems</u> are of a sensible <u>length</u>. That way, any hanging masses won't <u>hit the floor</u> or the <u>table</u> during the experiment.

4) When <u>heating</u> materials, make sure to let them <u>cool</u> before moving them, or wear <u>insulated gloves</u> while handling them. If you're using an <u>immersion heater</u> to heat liquids, you should always let it <u>dry out</u> in air, just in case any liquid has leaked inside the heater.

5) If you're using a <u>laser</u>, there are a few safety rules you must follow. Always wear <u>laser safety goggles</u> and never <u>look directly into</u> the laser or shine it <u>towards another person</u>. Make sure you turn the laser <u>off</u> if it's not needed to avoid any accidents.

6) When working with electronics, make sure you use a <u>low</u> enough <u>voltage</u> and <u>current</u> to prevent wires <u>overheating</u> (and potentially melting) and also to avoid <u>damaging components</u>, e.g. blowing a filament bulb.

7) You also need to be aware of <u>general safety</u> in the lab — handle <u>glassware</u> carefully so it doesn't <u>break</u>, don't stick your fingers in sockets and avoid touching frayed wires. That kind of thing.

BEWARE — hazardous physics experiments about...

Before you carry out an experiment, it's important to consider all of the <u>hazards</u>. Hazards can be anything from <u>lasers</u> to <u>electrical currents</u>, or <u>weights</u> to <u>heating equipment</u>. Whatever the hazards, make sure you know all the <u>safety precautions</u> you should follow to keep yourself <u>safe</u>.

Practice Exams

Once you've been through all the questions in this book, you should feel pretty confident about the exams.
As final preparation, here is a set of **practice exams** to really get you set for the real thing. The time allowed for
each paper is 1 hour 10 minutes. These papers are designed to give you the best possible preparation for your exams.

CGP Practice Exam Paper
GCSE Combined Science

GCSE Combined Science

Physics 1

Higher Tier

In addition to this paper you should have:
• A ruler.
• A calculator.

Centre name				
Centre number				
Candidate number				

Time allowed:
• 1 hour 10 minutes

Surname	
Other names	
Candidate signature	

Instructions to candidates
• Write your name and other details in the spaces provided above.
• Answer **all** questions in the spaces provided.
• Do all rough work on the paper.
• Cross out any work you do not want to be marked.
• You are allowed to use a calculator.

Information for candidates
• The marks available are given in brackets at the end of each question.
• There are 60 marks available for this paper.
• You should use good English and present your answers in a
clear and organised way.
• For questions marked with an asterisk (*) ensure that your answers
have a logical structure with points that link together clearly, and
include detailed, relevant information.

Advice to candidates
• In calculations show clearly how you worked out your answers.
• Read each question carefully before answering it.
• Check your answers if you have time.

For examiner's use

Q	Attempt Nº			Q	Attempt Nº		
	1	2	3		1	2	3
1				4			
2				5			
3				6			
				Total			

1 A group of students are investigating different types of energy transfer.

(a) One student heats a metal spoon over a Bunsen burner.

(i) Explain why the amount of energy transferred to the spoon and its surroundings cannot be greater than the amount of energy transferred from the Bunsen burner.

....

....

[1 mark]

(ii) Which energy store of the gas is energy being transferred from as the Bunsen is used?

☐ **A** Nuclear

☐ **B** Electrostatic

☐ **C** Chemical

☐ **D** Kinetic

[1 mark]

The student then uses tongs to place the hot spoon into an insulated flask full of cold water, like the one shown in **Figure 1**.
The insulated flask is then sealed.

Figure 1

(iii) The sealed flask can be treated as a closed system.
Which of the following statements is **true** for a closed system?

☐ **A** The net change in the energy of the system is always positive.

☐ **B** The net change in the energy of the system is always negative.

☐ **C** The net change in the energy of the system is always zero.

☐ **D** The net change in the energy of the system may be positive or negative.

[1 mark]

(b) Another student is investigating how much a rubber ball heats up when it is bounced. During his experiment:

1. The ball is thrown horizontally at a wall.
2. The ball hits the wall, causing it to deform and heat up.
3. The ball bounces back to the student.
4. The student repeatedly throws the ball at the wall.
5. Every 20 seconds, the student uses a thermometer to measure the temperature of the ball's surface.

(i) Suggest **one** way to improve the student's experiment.

....

[1 mark]

(ii) Describe the energy transfers that occur as the ball collides with the wall and moves away from the wall.

....

....

....

....

....

....

....

[4 marks]

(c) The experiment is changed so that now the ball is released from a height of 1.75 metres and allowed to fall vertically. The ball has a mass of 30 grams. The gravitational field strength of Earth is 10 N/kg.

Calculate the energy transferred from the GPE store as the ball falls 1.75 m. Use the equation:

change in GPE = mass × gravitational field strength × change in vertical height

Energy = ... J

[2 marks]

[Total 10 marks]

Turn over for the next question

Turn over ▶

2 A woman would like to make her home more energy efficient in order to reduce her impact on the environment.

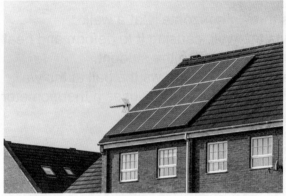

Figure 2

(a) **Figure 2** shows the solar panels she has fitted to her roof to generate electricity. Solar panels are an example of a renewable energy resource.

   (i) Give **one** other example of a renewable energy resource.

   ....
   [1 mark]

Each hour the Sun's rays transfer 1.2 MJ of energy to the solar panels' surfaces. Of this energy, 0.2 MJ is transferred away usefully.

   (ii) State the equation relating efficiency, total energy supplied to a device and useful energy transferred by the device.

   ....
   [1 mark]

   (iii) Calculate the efficiency of the home owner's solar panels.

   Efficiency = ...
   [2 marks]

(b) **Figure 3** shows a country's total energy use per year over 15 years.

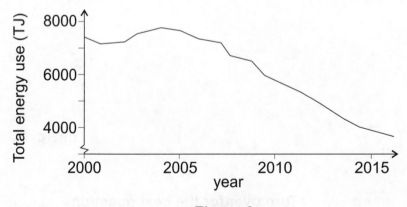

Figure 3

(i) Describe how the amount of energy used by the country has changed over time. Suggest **one** reason for this.

....

....

....

[2 marks]

The overall use of renewable resources in the country has increased over time.

(ii) Suggest **two** factors which might limit the use of renewable energy resources.

1. ....

2. ....

[2 marks]

(c) The home owner wants to build an extension.
The extension will be built with walls that are a single brick thick.
She is trying to decide which type of brick to use to build the extension walls.
Figure 4 shows some types of brick that she could use.

Brick	Volume (cm³)	Thickness (cm)	Thermal Conductivity (W/mK)
Brick X	150	8	0.84
Brick Y	150	12	0.62
Brick Z	150	10	0.84

Figure 4

Suggest which type of brick the home owner should use to minimise the rate of cooling of the extension. Justify your answer.

....

....

....

....

....

[3 marks]

[Total 11 marks]

Turn over for the next question

Turn over ▶

3 **Figure 5** shows a couple doing a dance routine on an ice rink.

Figure 5

At the start of the routine, the woman is at the entrance to the ice rink.

Figure 6 shows her distance-time graph for the first 35 seconds of the routine.

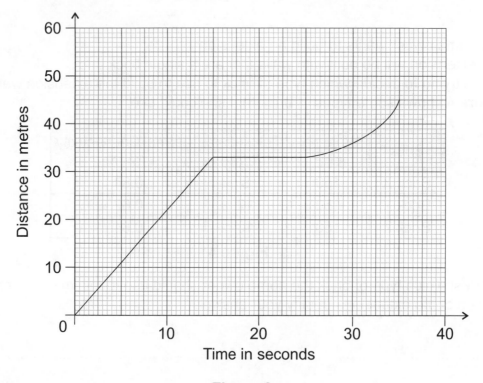

Figure 6

(a) Describe the motion of the woman during the first 35 seconds of the routine.

....

....

....

....

[3 marks]

(b) After travelling 33 m the woman arrives at the centre of the rink.
Use **Figure 6** to determine the speed of the woman as she travels to the centre of the rink.

Speed = ... m/s
[2 marks]

The man is travelling at a constant speed of 3.5 metres per second.

(c) (i) State the equation relating speed, distance and time.

[1 mark]

(ii) Calculate the time it will take the man to travel a distance of 14 metres.

Time = ... s
[3 marks]

(d) The man then brings himself to a complete stop in 7 seconds.

(i) Which of the following options is the correct value of his average deceleration?

☐ **A** 0.5 m/s²

☐ **B** 7 m/s²

☐ **C** 10 m/s²

☐ **D** 24.5 m/s²

[1 mark]

(ii) Compare the magnitudes of the driving forces and the frictional forces acting on the man as he decelerates.

....

....
[1 mark]
[Total 11 marks]

Turn over for the next question

Turn over ▶

4 A student wants to investigate how much different transparent materials will refract a beam of light. She has three rectangular blocks made out of different transparent materials, similar to the one shown in **Figure 7**.

Figure 7

(a) Describe an experiment the student could carry out in order to investigate this.

....

....

....

....

[3 marks]

(b) (i) Name a piece of equipment that the student could use to create a thin beam of light.

....

[1 mark]

(ii) Explain **one** advantage of using a thin beam of light.

....

....

[1 mark]

(c) **Figure 8** shows the angles of refraction for three different materials, for a fixed angle of incidence.

Material	Angle of refraction (°)
Ice	37
Flint glass	24
Acrylic	31

Figure 8

(i) State the material in which light travels the slowest.

....

[1 mark]

(ii) Explain your answer to part **(i)**.

....

....

[2 marks]

(d) When light of frequency 5.1×10^{14} Hz is travelling through flint glass, the wavelength of the light is 353 nm.

Calculate the speed of light in flint glass.

Speed of light in flint glass = ... m/s

[2 marks]

[Total 10 marks]

Turn over for the next question

Turn over ▶

5 ***(a)** Models of the atom have developed over time.

Figure 9 shows an early model of the atom, Model X, and a currently used model of the atom, Model Y.

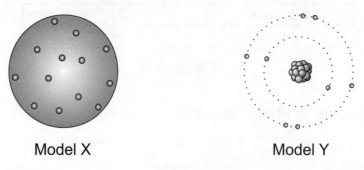

Model X   Model Y

Figure 9

Explain how experiments and scientific discoveries caused our understanding of the atom to develop from Model X to Model Y.
Your answer should include descriptions of the models shown in **Figure 10**.

....

....

....

....

....

....

....

....

[6 marks]

(b) (i) An unstable atom will emit radiation.

A student places a detector next to a radioactive sample of bismuth-212.
She records the count-rate measured by the detector every 10 seconds.

Name a detector that the student could use to measure the count-rate.

....

[1 mark]

(ii) Bismuth-212 can decay by beta-minus emission to form an isotope of polonium (Po).
Figure 10 shows an incomplete nuclear equation showing this decay.

$$^{212}_{83}\text{Bi} \rightarrow ^{212}_{A}\text{Po} + ^{0}_{B}\beta$$

Figure 10

Determine the atomic number, A, of the polonium atom.

A = ...

[1 mark]

(iii) The student plots a graph of the count-rate of the bismuth-212 sample against time.

Figure 11 shows the student's graph.

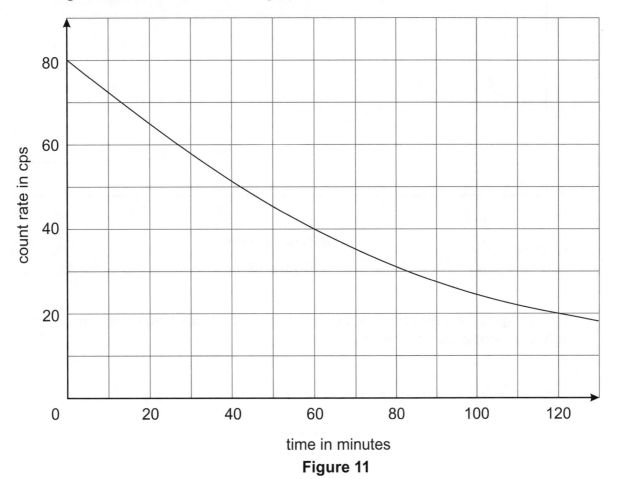

time in minutes

Figure 11

Use **Figure 11** to calculate the half-life of bismuth-212.
Give your answer in minutes.

Half-life = ... minutes
[2 marks]

Question 5 continues on the next page

Turn over ▶

(c) Another radioactive isotope, iodine-131, emits gamma rays.

Iodine-131 is typically stored in a lead-lined box.

Figure 12 shows the radiation detected outside the box against the thickness of the box's lead lining.

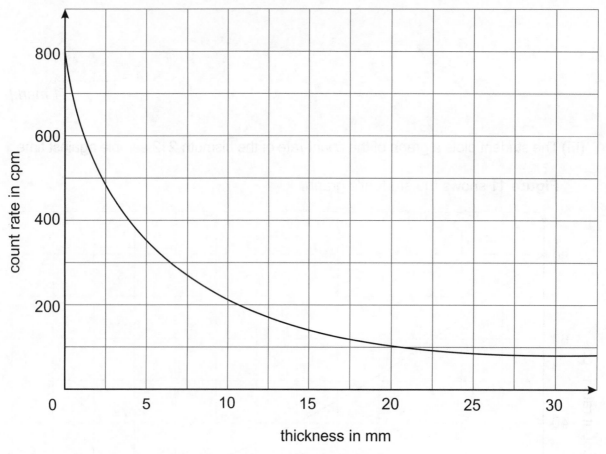

thickness in mm

Figure 12

Using **Figure 12**, describe how the thickness of the box's lead lining affects the safety of people near to the box.

....

....

....

[2 marks]

[Total 12 marks]

6 A student is investigating sound waves. Her experimental set-up is shown in **Figure 13**.

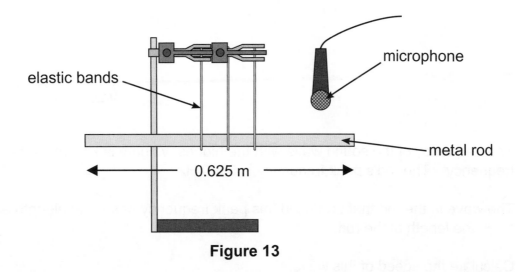

Figure 13

A 0.625 m metal rod is suspended by elastic bands.

The student strikes the metal rod with a hammer in order to produce a sound.
The sound that is produced is made up of sound waves of a range of frequencies.

A microphone connected to a computer records and measures the volume of all the sound waves produced by the metal rod.

The experiment is repeated three times and the measurements of volume are averaged.
Figure 14 shows the student's results.

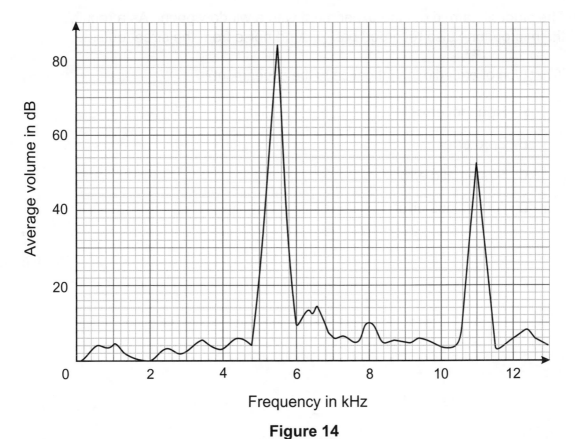

Figure 14

Question 6 continues on the next page

Turn over ▶

(a) What was the average volume of the 8 kHz sound wave produced by the rod?

Volume = ... dB

[1 mark]

(b) The frequency of the sound wave with the highest volume is known as the 'peak frequency'. The rod's peak frequency is 5500 Hz.

The wave in the rod that produced this peak frequency has a wavelength equal to twice the length of the rod.

Calculate the speed of this wave.
Give you answer to 2 significant figures.

Wave speed = ... m/s

[4 marks]

(c) The student carried out the experiment with a window open. As a result, the microphone also recorded background noise from the street outside.

What type of error did this introduce to the experiment?

☐ **A** Random error

☐ **B** Zero error

☐ **C** Systematic error

☐ **D** Anomalous error

[1 mark]

[Total 6 marks]

END OF QUESTIONS

CGP Practice Exam Paper
GCSE Combined Science

GCSE Combined Science

Physics 2
Higher Tier

In addition to this paper you should have:
*   A ruler.
*   A calculator.

Centre name				
Centre number				
Candidate number				

Time allowed:
*   1 hour 10 minutes

Surname	
Other names	
Candidate signature	

Instructions to candidates
*   Write your name and other details in the spaces provided above.
*   Answer **all** questions in the spaces provided.
*   Do all rough work on the paper.
*   Cross out any work you do not want to be marked.
*   You are allowed to use a calculator.

Information for candidates
*   The marks available are given in brackets at the end of each question.
*   There are 60 marks available for this paper.
*   You should use good English and present your answers in a clear and organised way.
*   For questions marked with an asterisk (*) ensure that your answers have a logical structure with points that link together clearly, and include detailed, relevant information.

Advice to candidates
*   In calculations show clearly how you worked out your answers.
*   Read each question carefully before answering it.
*   Check your answers if you have time.

For examiner's use

Q	Attempt Nº 1	2	3	Q	Attempt Nº 1	2	3
1				4			
2				5			
3				6			
Total							

1   **Figure 1** shows a kettle that uses electricity to boil water.

Figure 1

(a) (i) Which of the following equations correctly relates charge, current and time?

☐ **A** charge = current × time

☐ **B** charge = ½ × current × time

☐ **C** charge = current ÷ time

☐ **D** charge = time ÷ current

[1 mark]

(ii) The current through the kettle is 12 A.
Calculate the time taken for 1440 C to pass through the kettle.

Time = ... s

[3 marks]

(b) The kettle has a power rating of 3000 W.
Explain what the term power rating means.

....

....

....

[1 mark]

(c) When the kettle is heating water, energy is transferred electrically from the mains to the heating element of the kettle.

Describe the energy transfer that occurs between the heating element and the water in the kettle.

....

....

....

....

....

[3 marks]

(d) To bring a full kettle of water to the boil, 740 kJ of energy is transferred to the kettle. 680 kJ of this energy is usefully transferred to the water.

Using this information, complete the energy transfer diagram in **Figure 2** for bringing a full kettle of water to the boil.

Label the diagram with the correct values for the energy transferred.

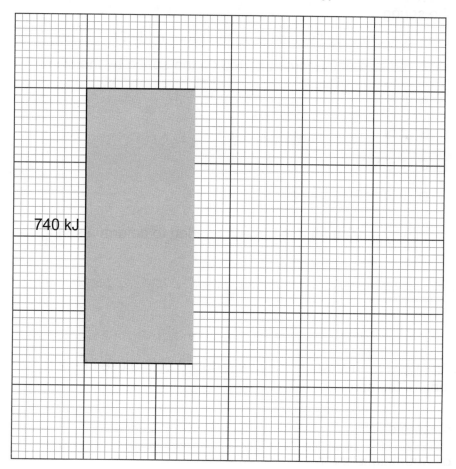

740 kJ

Figure 2

[2 marks]

[Total 10 marks]

Turn over for the next question

Turn over ▶

2 A student is given a set of apparatus, set up as shown in **Figure 3**.
The hook is assumed to have zero mass.

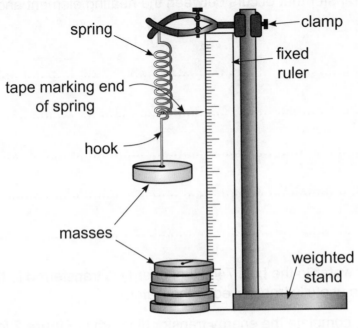

Figure 3

(a) (i) Placing one of the masses on the hook exerts a force of 1 N on the bottom
of the spring.

A force is exerted by the clamp on the other end of the spring.

What is the size of the force exerted on the spring by the clamp?

☐ **A** 0.5 N

☐ **B** 1 N

☐ **C** 1.5 N

☐ **D** 2 N

[1 mark]

(ii) Explain why more than one force is needed to deform a spring.

....

....

[1 mark]

(b) Name the type of error which may be reduced by the use of the tape marker
at the end of the spring.

☐ **A** zero error

☐ **B** anomalous error

☐ **C** systematic error

☐ **D** random error

[1 mark]

*(c) Describe how the student could use the experimental set-up in **Figure 3** to find the spring constant of the spring.

....

....

....

....

....

....

....

....

....

....

....

....

[6 marks]

(d) The student used the apparatus in **Figure 3** to produce the graph shown in **Figure 4**.

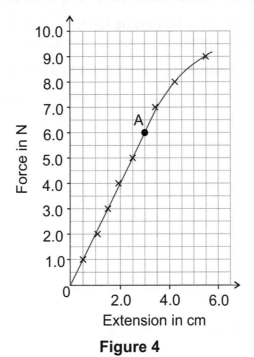

Figure 4

Question 2 continues on the next page

Turn over ▶

Calculate the work done to stretch the spring to point A.

Work done = ... J

[3 marks]

(e) The student then decided to use his apparatus to create a force-extension graph for a rubber band. The student's graph is shown in **Figure 5**.

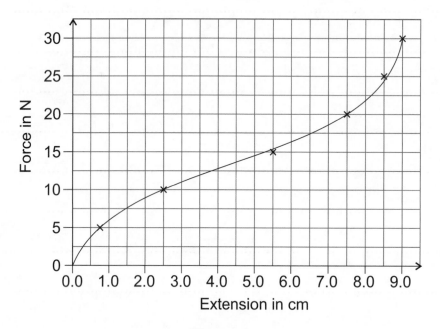

Figure 5

Before the experiment, the student made the following statement:

"I think that rubber bands will behave elastically when stretched.
I also think the relationship between force and extension will be linear."

After the experiment, the rubber band returned to its original shape and size.

Discuss the extent to which the student's statement is supported by the results of the experiment.

....

....

....

....

....

[2 marks]

[Total 14 marks]

3 A student has a length of wire.

(a) Which of the following shows the magnetic field around the wire when a current flows through the wire? The current is flowing into the paper.

☐ **A**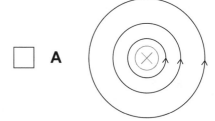

☐ **B**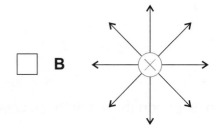

☐ **C**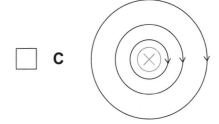

☐ **D**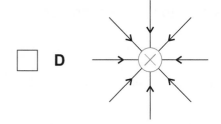

[1 mark]

(b) The current flowing through the wire is 2.4 A.
Calculate the amount of charge that will have flowed through the wire in 30 minutes.

Charge = ... C
[2 marks]

Question 3 continues on the next page

Turn over ▶

(c) The student passes the wire between the poles of two magnets, as shown in **Figure 6**. The magnetic field between the poles has a magnetic flux density of 0.75 T. The length of wire inside the magnetic field is 0.05 m.

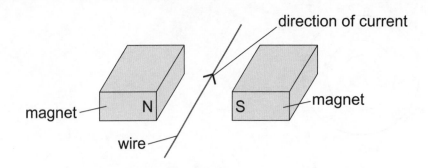

Figure 6

Calculate the size of the force on the wire.

Use the correct equation from the Physics Equation Sheet on the inside back cover.

Force = ... N

[2 marks]

(d) Suggest **one** way the student could change their set-up to increase the size of the force on the wire.

....

....

[1 mark]

[Total 6 marks]

4 A student wants to investigate the relationship between current and potential difference for a fixed resistor.

The student has:

- a battery
- a fixed resistor
- a variable resistor
- an ammeter
- a voltmeter

(a) **Figure 7** is an incomplete circuit diagram of the circuit the student uses in their experiment. Complete **Figure 7**.

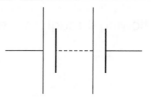

Figure 7

[3 marks]

Question 4 continues on the next page

Turn over ▶

(b) The student carries out her experiment three times.
Figure 8 is a table of the student's measurements.

Potential Difference across resistor (V)	Current through resistor (A)		
	Test 1	Test 2	Test 3
0.0	0.00	0.00	0.00
1.0	0.52	0.51	0.50
2.0	0.99	0.99	1.00
3.0	1.52	1.50	1.50
4.0	1.98	1.99	1.99
5.0	2.53	2.52	2.51

Figure 8

Calculate the mean current flowing through the resistor when the potential difference across it was 5.0 V.

Current = ... A

[1 mark]

(c) The student notices that over time, the resistor being tested feels warm.
This is because energy is transferred when work is done against electrical resistance.

In terms of electrons and ions, explain the cause of this energy transfer in the resistor.

....

....

....

....

....

[2 marks]

(d) The student tests another fixed resistor, which has a resistance of 2 Ω.
Calculate the potential difference that needs to be applied across the resistor to cause a current of 5 A to flow through the resistor.

Potential difference = ... V

[2 marks]

(e) The student uses a similar experiment to investigate the relationship between current and potential difference in a filament lamp.

She then plots her results on a graph of current against potential difference.

What should the graph of her results look like?

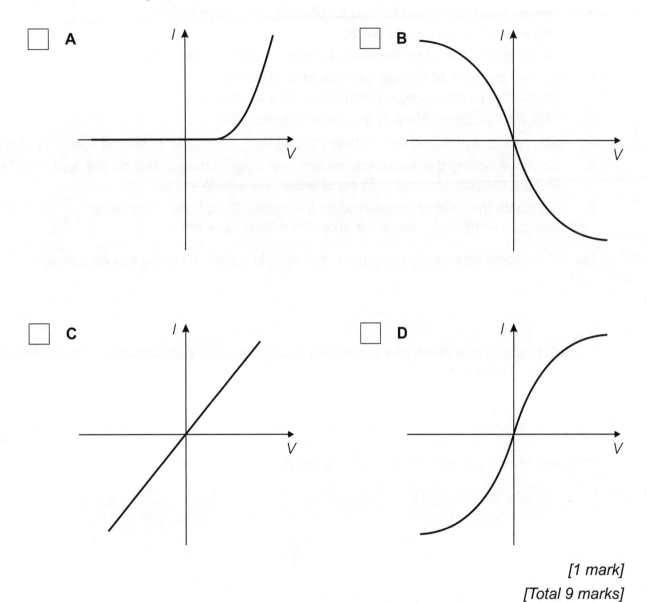

☐ A

☐ B

☐ C

☐ D

[1 mark]

[Total 9 marks]

Turn over for the next question

5 A student is investigating the energy needed to boil different masses of water.
This is their method:

1. Place an empty beaker on a mass balance and zero the balance.
2. Add 0.25 kg of water to the beaker.
3. Use a clamp and stand to hold an electric immersion heater and a thermometer in the water.
4. Keeping the beaker on the mass balance, switch on the heater.
5. Record the current through and potential difference across the heater using an ammeter and a voltmeter.
6. Wait for the temperature of the water to reach 100 °C.
7. Start a stopwatch and record how long it takes the heater to boil off 0.025 kg of water.
8. Continue boiling the water, and record how long it takes to boil off the next 0.025 kg. Repeat the process until 0.05 kg of water remains in the beaker.
9. Calculate the energy transferred by the heater to boil the water using:
energy transferred = current × potential difference × time.

(a) (i) Suggest **one** safety precaution that should be taken during this experiment.

....
[1 mark]

(ii) Suggest **one** piece of equipment the student could use instead of the ammeter and voltmeter.

....
[1 mark]

Figure 9 shows a graph of the student's results.

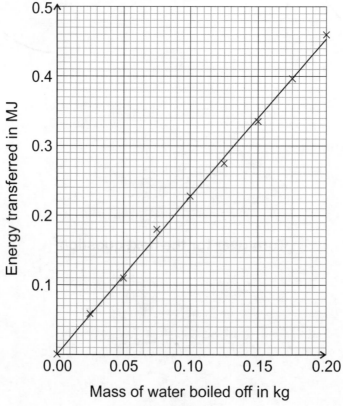

Figure 9

(b) Use **Figure 9** to determine the specific latent heat of vaporisation for water.

Specific latent heat = ... MJ/kg

[2 marks]

(c) The electric immersion heater had a potential difference of 12 V across it.
The current through the heater was 8 A.

Using **Figure 9**, how long had the water been boiling for when 0.185 kg of water had boiled off?

You can assume that no energy was transferred from the water to the surroundings, and that the immersion heater was 100% efficient.

Use the correct equation from the Physics Equation Sheet on the inside back cover.

☐ **A** 4375 s

☐ **B** 4271 s

☐ **C** 40 s

☐ **D** 35 000 s

[1 mark]

(d) Describe **one** difference between particles in liquid water and particles in water vapour.

....

....

[1 mark]

[Total 6 marks]

Turn over for the next question

Turn over ▶

6   A student sets up the circuit shown in **Figure 10**.

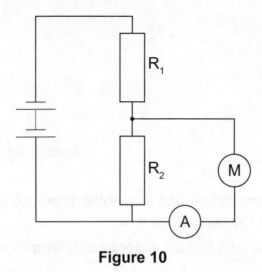

Figure 10

(a) (i) State the equation that links electrical power, current and potential difference.

....

[1 mark]

(ii) The battery used in the circuit is a 12 V battery.
The potential difference across R_1 is 4.0 V.
The current through R_1 is 5.0 A. The current through R_2 is 3.0 A.
Calculate the power of the motor.

Power = ... W

[3 marks]

(b) The motor is attached to fan blades.
The student decides to investigate how fast the fan blades will spin when different motors are used.

The student draws a graph of the speed of the blades over time for three different motors, as shown in **Figure 11**. All the motors have the same efficiency.

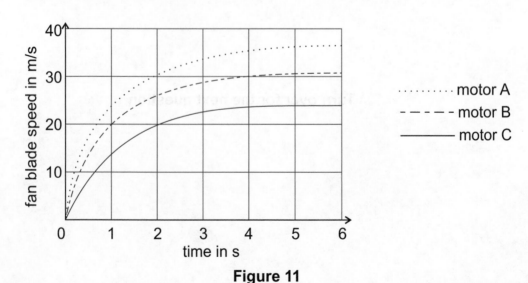

Figure 11

(i) Explain which motor has the highest power.

....

....

....
[3 marks]

(ii) Suggest one way to reduce energy losses from the motors.

....
[1 mark]

(c) The student creates a sensing circuit to control an electric heater, as shown in **Figure 12**.

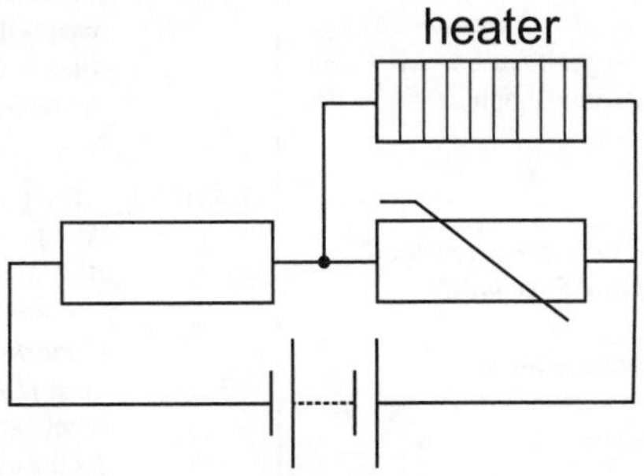

Figure 12

Explain what will happen to the potential difference across the heater as the room temperature increases.

....

....

....
[3 marks]

(d) The electric heater is used to heat 2.1 kg of water.
The water is heated from 16 °C to 65 °C.
The specific heat capacity of water is 4200 J/kg°C.

The heater is 85% efficient.
Calculate the energy transferred to the heater when it is used to heat the water.
Use the correct equation from the Physics Equation Sheet on the inside back cover.

Energy transferred = ... J
[4 marks]
[Total 15 marks]

END OF QUESTIONS

Answers

Section 1 — Motion and Forces

Page 24
Warm-Up Questions
1   Speed is scalar, velocity is a vector /
    velocity has a direction, speed does not.
2 a)   E.g. 3 m/s
   b)   E.g. 250 m/s
   c)   E.g. 340 m/s
Your answers may be slightly different to these, but as long as they're about the same size, you should be fine to use them in the exam.
3   Velocity is calculated from the gradient.
4   A straight, horizontal line.

Exam Questions
1 a)   The cyclist travels at a constant speed
         (of 3 m/s) between 5 s and 8 s *[1 mark]*,
         then decelerates between 8 s and 10 s *[1 mark]*.
   b)   Area of triangle = 0.5 × width × height
        Width = 5 − 2 = 3 s
        Height = 3 m/s
        Distance = 0.5 × 3 × 3 = **4.5 m**
        [2 marks for correct answer, otherwise 1 mark for a correct method to calculate the area under the graph between 2 and 5 seconds]
You can also answer this question by counting the number of squares under the graph between 2 and 5 s — there are 4.5 squares, and the area of one square is equivalent to 1 m (height of one square × width of one square = 1 m/s × 1 s), so the cyclist has travelled 4.5 m.
   c)   Acceleration is given by the gradient of a velocity-time graph.
        change in y = 3 − 0 = 3 m/s
        change in x = 5 − 2 = 3 s
        acceleration = 3 ÷ 3 = **1 m/s²**
        [2 marks for correct answer, otherwise 1 mark for a correct method to calculate the gradient of the line between 2 and 5 seconds]
You could also have used $a = (v - u) ÷ t$ here.
   d)   average acceleration = change in velocity ÷ change in time /
        $a = (v − u) ÷ t$
        velocity at 8 s = 3 m/s; velocity at 10 s = 2 m/s
        so $v − u$ = 2 − 3 = −1 m/s
        So, a = −1 ÷ 2
              = −0.5 m/s²
        So, deceleration = **0.5 m/s²**
        [3 marks for correct answer, otherwise 1 mark for correct calculation of change in velocity and 1 mark for correct substitution]
Your answer should be positive since the question asks for deceleration, rather than acceleration.
2 a)   E.g. 31 m/s *[1 mark]*
   b) i)   acceleration = change in velocity ÷ change in time
           $a = (v − u) ÷ t$
           $v − u$ = 31 − 0 = 31 m/s
           a = 31 ÷ 5
              = **6.2 m/s²**
           [2 marks for correct answer, otherwise 1 mark for correct substitution]
      ii) $v^2 − u^2 = 2 × a × x$
            rearrange for x
            $x = (v^2 − u^2) ÷ (2 × a)$
              = $(31^2 − 0^2) ÷ (2 × 6.2)$
              = **77.5 m**
              = **78 m (to 2 s.f.)**
            [3 marks for correct answer, otherwise 1 mark for correct rearrangement and 1 mark for correct substitution]
Even if you got the answer to (a) wrong, award yourself the marks for (b) if you did the sums above correctly.

Page 27
Warm-Up Questions
1   0 N
2   force = mass × acceleration
This is Newton's Second Law.
3   false
4   Boulder B
Boulder B needs a greater force to accelerate it by the same amount as boulder A.
5   true
This is Newton's Third Law.

Exam Questions
1 a)   The ball exerts a force of −500 N on the bat *[1 mark]*, because, from Newton's Third Law, if the bat exerts a force on the ball, the ball exerts an equal force on the bat in the opposite direction *[1 mark]*.
   b)   The acceleration of the ball is greater *[1 mark]* because it has a smaller mass, but is acted on by the same size force (and $F = m × a$) *[1 mark]*.

2 a)   Force = mass × acceleration / $F = m × a$
        So, $a = F ÷ m$
        Set direction of van's motion to be positive, so F = −200 N
        a = −200 ÷ 2500
           = −0.08 m/s²
        So, deceleration = **0.08 m/s²**
        [3 marks for correct answer, otherwise 1 mark for correct rearrangement and 1 mark for correct substitution]
   b)   Force = mass × acceleration / $F = m × a$
        F = 4.50 × 28.0
           = **126 N**
        [2 marks for correct answer, otherwise 1 mark for correct substitution]
   c)   By Newton's Third Law, force on van due to the cone in the collision is −126 N.
        force = mass × acceleration / $F = m × a$
        So, $a = F ÷ m$
        a = −126 ÷ 2500
           = −0.0504 m/s²
        So deceleration = **0.0504 m/s²**
        [3 marks for correct answer, otherwise 1 mark for correct rearrangement and 1 mark for correct substitution]
You'd still get the marks here, even if you got (b) wrong, as long as your method's correct.

Page 31
Warm-Up Questions
1   It means that the force due to gravity caused by the hanging mass will be the main cause of the trolley accelerating.
2   Mass is the amount of 'stuff' in an object. Weight is the force acting on an object due to gravity.
3   Newtons

Exam Questions
1   Weight = mass × gravitational field strength / $W = m × g$
    W = 80 × 10
       = **800 N**
    [2 marks for correct answer, otherwise 1 mark for correct substitution]
2 a)   mass *[1 mark]*
   b)   acceleration *[1 mark]*
   c)   As the mass increases, the acceleration decreases at a decreasing rate / mass and acceleration are inversely proportional *[1 mark]*.
3 a) $W = m × g$, so if the weight of an object on Mars is 0.4 times its weight on Earth, then Mars's gravitational field strength must be 0.4 times Earth's gravitational field strength (since mass is constant).
        0.4 × 10 = **4 N/kg**
        [2 marks for correct answer, otherwise 1 mark for correct reasoning of gravitational field strength being 0.4 times the gravitational field strength on Earth]
   b) $W = m × g$
        $m = W ÷ g$
          = 3600 ÷ 4
          = **900 kg**
        [3 marks for correct answer, otherwise 1 mark for correct rearrangement and 1 mark for correct substitution]
Even if you got the answer to (a) wrong, you get full marks for (b) if you did the calculations correctly with your answer for (a).
4   How to grade your answer:
    Level 0:   There is no relevant information. *[No marks]*
    Level 1:   A simple experiment to investigate force and acceleration which can be performed with the given equipment is partly outlined.
               The answer lacks structure. *[1 to 2 marks]*
    Level 2:   An experiment to investigate force and acceleration which can be performed with the given equipment is outlined in some detail.
               The answer has some structure. *[3 to 4 marks]*
    Level 3:   An experiment to investigate force and acceleration which can be performed with the given equipment is fully described in detail.
               The answer is well structured. *[5 to 6 marks]*
    Here are some points your answer may include:
    Place all of the masses on the trolley.
    Calculate the weight of the hanging hook using $W = m × g$ — this is the accelerating force.
    Place the trolley on the ramp and adjust the height of the ramp until the trolley just starts to move.
    Mark a line on the ramp just before the first light gate.
    Hold the trolley at the start line and release the trolley, so that it moves through the light gates.
    Record the time and velocity as the trolley passes through each light gate.
    Calculate and record the trolley's acceleration using $a = (v − u) ÷ t$.
    Take one of the masses from the trolley, and add it to the hook.

Repeat the steps above (starting with calculating the new total weight of the hanging hook) until all the masses from the trolley have been moved to the hook.
Plot the results on a graph of acceleration against accelerating force (the total weight of the hook), and draw a line of best fit.

Page 35
Warm-Up Questions
1.   kg m/s
2.   In a closed system, the total momentum before an interaction must equal the total momentum after the interaction.
3.   The total momentum is zero.
4.   It decreases the force.

Exam Questions
1   a)   momentum = mass × velocity / $p = m \times v$ *[1 mark]*
   b) $p = 60 \times 5.0$
          = **300 kg m/s**
          [2 marks for correct answer,
          otherwise 1 mark for correct substitution]
   c)   force = change in momentum ÷ time / $F = (mv - mu) \div t$
          Gymnast comes to a stop, so change in momentum = 300 kg m/s
          $F = 300 \div 1.2$
          = **250 N**
          [2 marks for correct answer, otherwise 1 mark for correct substitution]
2   a)   momentum = mass × velocity / $p = m \times v$
          $p = 650 \times 15.0$
          = **9750 kg m/s**
          [2 marks for correct answer,
          otherwise 1 mark for correct substitution]
   b)   momentum before = momentum after
          momentum of first car = 9750 kg m/s
          momentum of second car = 750 × (–10.0)
                             = –7500 kg m/s
          Total momentum before = 9750 + (–7500)
                          = 2250 kg m/s
          Total momentum after = (mass of car 1 + mass of car 2) × v
          2250 = (650 + 750) × v
          so, v = 2250 ÷ (650 + 750)
                 = 2250 ÷ 1400
                 = 1.607142...
                 = **1.61 m/s (to 3 s.f.)**
          [4 marks for correct answer, otherwise 1 mark for correct calculation of total momentum before the collision, 1 mark for correctly equating momentum before and after the collision and 1 mark for correct unrounded answer]
3   momentum before = momentum after
          momentum of neutron before = 1 × 14 000
                                 = 14 000
          momentum of uranium before = 235 × 0
                                 = 0
          momentum of neutron after = 1 × –13 000
                              = –13 000
          momentum of uranium after = 235 × v
          So, 14 000 = –13 000 + 235 × v
          so, v = (14 000 + 13 000) ÷ 235
                = 114.8936...
                = **115 km/s (to 3 s.f.)**
          [4 marks for correct answer, otherwise 1 mark for correct calculations of momentum, 1 mark for correctly equating momentum before and after the collision and 1 mark for correct unrounded answer]
Don't worry too much about the units in this question. The masses given are relative masses, with no units, so we couldn't use the standard units for momentum. As you're only looking for the velocity though, you can just do the calculation as normal, and make sure that the units on your final answer match the units for velocity given in the question.

Page 39
Warm-Up Questions
1.   Get the individual to sit with their arm resting on the edge of a table. Hold a ruler end-down so that the 0 cm mark hangs between their thumb and forefinger. Drop the ruler without warning. The individual must grab the ruler between their thumb and forefinger as quickly as possible. Measure the distance at which they have caught the ruler. Use $v^2 - u^2 = 2 \times a \times x$ and $a = 10$ m/s² to calculate v, and $a = (v - u) \div t$ to calculate the time taken for the ruler to fall that distance. This is their reaction time.
2.   The thinking distance is the distance travelled during a person's reaction time (the time between seeing a hazard, and applying the brakes).
3.   The braking distance.
4.   Any one from: e.g. poor grip on the roads increases braking distance / poor visibility delays when you see the hazard / distraction by the weather delays when you see the hazard.
5.   Crumple zones increase collision time, which reduces the force on the vehicle and passengers (since $F = (mv - mu) \div t$). This reduces the risk of harm in a crash.

Exam Question
1   a)   stopping distance = braking distance + thinking distance,
          So, braking distance = stopping distance – thinking distance
          At 40 mph,
          stopping distance = 35 m (accept between 34 m and 36 m)
          thinking distance = 12 m (accept between 11 m and 13 m)
          braking distance = 35 – 12 = **23 m**
          (Accept correct for above readings)
          [3 marks for correct answer, otherwise 1 mark for correctly reading stopping and thinking distances from the graph and 1 mark for correct substitution]
   b)   braking distance *[1 mark]*
The stopping distance is over twice as high as the thinking distance at 50 mph, so the braking distance must be bigger than the thinking distance.
   c)   Stopping distance is not directly proportional to speed. If stopping distance and speed were directly proportional, the relationship between them would be shown by a straight line / would be linear *[1 mark]*.
   d)   If the road were icy, the thinking distance graph would not change *[1 mark]* but the stopping distance graph would get steeper (as the braking distance would increase) *[1 mark]*.
The thinking distance graph doesn't change, because the icy road won't change your reaction time. But it will decrease the friction between the car and the road, so the braking distance increases.

Section 2 — Conservation of Energy

Page 44
Warm-Up Questions
1.   kinetic energy = ½ × mass × (speed)² / $KE = \frac{1}{2} \times m \times v^2$
2.   A lorry travelling at 60 miles per hour.
3.   Any two from: e.g. mechanically (by a force doing work) / electrically (work done by a charge) / by heating / by radiation.
4.   Energy is transferred by radiation to the thermal energy store of the water.

Exam Questions
1   a)   Change in gravitational potential energy = mass × gravitational field strength × change in height /
          $\Delta GPE = m \times g \times \Delta h$ *[1 mark]*
          So, $\Delta h = \Delta GPE \div (m \times g)$
                = 140 ÷ (20 × 10)
                = **0.7 m**
          [3 marks for the correct answer, otherwise 1 mark for correct rearrangement and 1 mark for correct substitution]
   b)   Energy is transferred from the gravitational potential energy store *[1 mark]* to the kinetic energy store of the load *[1 mark]*.
   c)   Some of the energy would also be transferred to the thermal energy store of the air (and the thermal energy store of the load) *[1 mark]*.
2   a)   Energy is transferred mechanically from the elastic potential energy store of the sling-shot *[1 mark]* to the kinetic energy store of the rock *[1 mark]*. This energy is then transferred mechanically to the gravitational potential energy store of the rock as it rises *[1 mark]*.
   b)   Kinetic energy = ½ × mass × (speed)² / $KE = \frac{1}{2} \times m \times v^2$
          $KE = \frac{1}{2} \times 0.06 \times (18)^2$
                = **9.72 J**
                = **9.7 J (to 2 s.f.)**
          [2 marks for correct answer, otherwise 1 mark for correct substitution]
   c)   At B all energy from the kinetic store has been transferred to the gravitational potential energy store.
          So, ΔGPE = 9.72 J
          $\Delta GPE = m \times g \times \Delta h$
          $\Delta h = \Delta GPE \div (m \times g)$
              = 9.72 ÷ (0.06 × 10)
              = **16.2 m**
          [3 marks for the correct answer, otherwise 1 mark for correct rearrangement and 1 mark for correct substitution]

Page 48
Warm-Up Questions
1.   Thermal energy stores.
2.   Some energy is always dissipated, so less than 100% of the energy supplied to a device is transferred usefully.
3.   E.g. lubrication
4.   The higher the thermal conductivity, the greater the rate of the energy transfer (i.e. the faster energy is transferred) through it.
5.   The thicker the walls, the slower the rate of cooling.

Exam Questions
1   a)   efficiency = useful energy transferred by the device ÷
                           total energy supplied to the device *[1 mark]*
   b)   efficiency = 480 ÷ 1200
                = **0.4 (or 40%)**
          [2 marks for correct answer, otherwise 1 mark for correct substitution]

c) efficiency = useful energy transferred by the device ÷
total energy supplied to the device

total energy supplied to the device
= useful energy transferred by the device ÷ efficiency
= 10 ÷ 0.55
= 18.181... = 18 J (to 2 s.f)
[3 marks for the correct answer, otherwise 1 mark for correct
rearrangement and 1 mark for correct substitution]

d) Disagree. Torch B has a lower input energy transfer than torch A, i.e.
it transfers less energy per minute than torch A (as 18.181... × 60 =
1090.9..., and 1090.9... < 1200) *[1 mark]*.

Even if you got the answer to (c) wrong, if your conclusion is correct for your answer to (d),
you'd get the marks for this question.

2 Best: C   Second best: B   Worst: A *[1 mark]*
The thicker a sample is, the slower the rate of energy transfer through it
so sample B will be a better insulator than sample A *[1 mark]*. Air has a
lower thermal conductivity than glass (so it transfers energy at a slower
rate than glass does) *[1 mark]* so even though samples B and C are the
same thickness, sample C is a better insulator than sample B *[1 mark]*.

Page 53
Warm-Up Questions
1 Any three from: coal / oil / natural gas / nuclear fuel (plutonium or
uranium).
2 Advantage: e.g. low running costs / won't run out / doesn't create
pollution
Disadvantage: e.g. cannot produce energy at night.
3 Any two from: e.g. it releases greenhouse gases and contributes to global
warming / it causes acid rain / coal mining damages the landscape.
4 Any two from: e.g. renewable resources don't currently provide enough
energy / energy from renewables cannot be relied upon currently / it's
expensive to build new renewable power plants / it's expensive to switch
to cars running on renewable energy.

Exam Questions
1 a) Solar *[1 mark]*, bio-fuels *[1 mark]*
b) E.g. flooding a valley for a dam can destroy habitats for some species
[1 mark].
c) E.g. they cause no pollution *[1 mark]*
2 a) Seconds in 5 hours = 5 × 60 × 60 = 18 000 s
Energy provided by 1 m² solar panel in 5 hours = 200 × 18 000
= 3 600 000 J
Number of panels needed = energy needed ÷ energy provided
= 32 500 000 ÷ 3 600 000
= 9.027... = **10 panels** (to next whole number)
[4 marks for correct answer, otherwise 1 mark for correct method of
calculation of energy provided by one panel, 1 mark for correct value
of energy provided by one panel and 1 mark for correct method of
calculation of number of panels needed]

Remember, because you have to have a set number of whole panels, if you get a decimal
answer, you need to round up to the next whole number to be able to provide the right
amount of energy.
b) Ten 1 m² solar panels are needed, so they will need at least 10 × 1 m² =
10 m² of space. However, they only have 8 m² of space on their roof, so
the family cannot install sufficient solar panels *[1 mark]*.
c) E.g. solar panels are less reliable than coal-fired power stations *[1 mark]*.
The energy output of the solar panels will vary based on the number of
hours of good sunlight, and may not be able to provide enough energy on
a given day *[1 mark]*. The energy output of coal-fired power stations is
not influenced by environmental factors like weather, and energy output
can be increased to meet demand *[1 mark]*.

Section 3 — Waves and the Electromagnetic Spectrum

Page 59
Warm-Up Questions
1 Waves only transfer energy and information, they do not transfer matter
(in this case, the twig and the water particles around the twig).
2 hertz (Hz)
3 e.g. sound / P-waves
4 wave speed = frequency × wavelength / $v = f \times \lambda$

Exam Questions
1 a) transverse *[1 mark]*
b) 5 cm *[1 mark]*
c) 2 m *[1 mark]*
d) It will halve *[1 mark]*.
$v = f \times \lambda$, so if f doubles, then λ must halve, so that v stays the same.

2 a) The distance he measures is 1 wavelength *[1 mark]*.
This can be used, together with the frequency
set by the signal generator, in the formula for wave speed,
wave speed = frequency × wavelength / $v = f \times \lambda$ *[1 mark]*.
b) wave speed = frequency × wavelength / $v = f \times \lambda$
So $v = 50 \times 6.8$
= 340 m/s
[2 marks for correct answer, otherwise 1 mark for correct substitution]

Page 62
Warm-Up Questions
1 reflection, transmission and absorption
2 false
The shorter the wavelength, the more an EM wave will be refracted as it hits a boundary
at an angle to the normal.
3 Away from the normal.
4 e.g. a ray box

Exam Questions
1 Diamond *[1 mark]* slows down the blue light by the greatest
amount, causing it to refract the most. *[1 mark]*
2 E.g. place the prism on a piece of paper and shine a ray of light at
the prism. Trace the incident and emergent rays and the boundaries
of the prism on the piece of paper *[1 mark]*. Remove the prism
and draw in the refracted ray through the prism by joining the
ends of the other two rays with a straight line *[1 mark]*. Draw
in the normals using a protractor and ruler *[1 mark]* and use the
protractor to measure *I* and *R* at both boundaries *[1 mark]*.

Page 69
Warm-Up Questions
1 transverse
2 false
All EM waves travel at the same speed in a vacuum.
3 gamma rays
4 true
5 e.g. communication / broadcasting / satellite transmissions
6 The microwaves penetrate a few centimetres into the food before being
absorbed by water molecules in the food. The microwaves transfer their
energy to the water molecules, causing the water to heat up. Energy is
then transferred from the water to the rest of the food by heating, causing
the food to cook.
7 infrared radiation
8 E.g. to sterilise medical equipment / to sterilise food / medical imaging /
cancer treatment.
9 true

Exam Questions
1 a) X-rays *[1 mark]*
b) E.g. could cause cancer / cell mutations / damage cells *[1 mark]*.
2 a) The incoming wave transfers energy to electrons in the receiver *[1 mark]*.
This causes the electrons to oscillate *[1 mark]*, generating an alternating
current in the circuit *[1 mark]*.
b) The resident shouldn't be concerned as radio waves have a very low
frequency so are not dangerous / are not absorbed by the body *[1 mark]*.
3 E.g. ultraviolet radiation is a type of ionising radiation, exposure to
this type of radiation can damage skin cells / could lead to skin cancer
[1 mark]. The damage to cells and risk of developing cancer could be
minimised by limiting the patient's exposure to the ultraviolet radiation
while still exposing her to enough so that it is an effective treatment
for her psoriasis *[1 mark]*. Exposure to ultraviolet radiation could also
damage the patient's eyes and cause a variety of eye conditions including
blindness *[1 mark]*. The risk of eye damage could be reduced by the
patient wearing protective goggles during treatments *[1 mark]*.

Section 4 — Radioactivity

Page 74
Warm-Up Questions
1 The atom consists of a sphere of positive charge throughout which
electrons are embedded like fruit in a plum pudding.
2 proton: 1, neutron: 1, electron: 0.0005
3 true
4 In the nucleus.
5 0; an atom has no overall charge.
6 1×10^{-10} m
7 false
An atom must lose an electron to become a positive ion.

Exam Questions

1 a)

	Proton	Electron	Neutron
Relative Charge	+1	-1	0
Number Present in Si-28	14	**14**	14

[2 marks — 1 mark for each correct answer]

b) Electrons may only occupy fixed energy levels *[1 mark]* at set distances from the nucleus *[1 mark]*.

c) 6.9×10^{-19} J *[1 mark]*

d) +1 *[1 mark]*

2 Most of the alpha particles passed straight through the gold foil *[1 mark]*. However, some were deflected back in the direction they came from *[1 mark]*. He concluded most of the atom is empty space *[1 mark]* whilst positive charge and mass is concentrated in a small nucleus *[1 mark]*.

Page 78

Warm-Up Questions

1 23 – 11 = 12 neutrons

2 false
Isotopes of an element will have identical atomic numbers and different mass numbers.

3 Any radiation that can knock electrons from atoms.

4 alpha

5 false
Gamma rays are stopped by thick sheets of lead or metres of concrete.

6 The atomic number will decrease by 1.

7 40
Mass number is unchanged by the emission of gamma radiation.

Exam Questions

1 Beta (particles) *[1 mark]*, because the radiation passes through the paper, but not the aluminium, so it is moderately penetrating in comparison to the other two *[1 mark]*.

2 a) The total number of protons and neutrons in the nucleus/atom. *[1 mark]*

b) Atom A and atom B *[1 mark]* because isotopes of the same element have the same atomic number, but different mass numbers *[1 mark]*.

c) $X = 86 - 2$
= **84** *[1 mark]*

Page 82

Warm-Up Questions

1 Any three from: e.g. the air / some foods / building materials / rocks / space / fallout from nuclear explosions / nuclear waste.

2 One decay occurs each second.

3 E.g. a Geiger-Müller tube

4 6 days.
To decrease by a factor of four, two half-lives must pass. 2 × 3 = 6.

5 Irradiation occurs when an object is exposed to radiation. Contamination occurs when a radioactive source gets onto or into an object.

6 To prevent your hands from becoming contaminated with radioactive materials / to prevent radioactive particles getting stuck to your skin or under your nails.

7 If you are exposed to alpha radiation from an external source (i.e. if you are irradiated), the alpha particles will be blocked by your skin. However, if an alpha source gets inside your body it can do a lot of damage to nearby cells, as it's strongly ionising.

Exam Questions

1 a) E.g. radiation sickness / cancer.
[2 marks — 1 mark for each correct answer]

b) Source A, because beta radiation is able to penetrate the skin and get to delicate organs *[1 mark]*.

c) E.g. store them in a lead-lined box *[1 mark]*.

2 a) 2 × 60 = 120 seconds
120 ÷ 40 = 3 half-lives
Activity after 1 half life: 8000 ÷ 2 = 4000,
Activity after 2 half lives: 4000 ÷ 2 = 2000,
Activity after 3 half lives: 2000 ÷ 2 = **1000 Bq**
[2 marks for correct answer, otherwise 1 mark for correctly calculating the number of half-lives]

b) Activity after 1 half life: 8000 ÷ 2 = 4000,
Activity after 2 half lives: 4000 ÷ 2 = 2000,
Activity after 3 half lives: 2000 ÷ 2 = 1000 Bq,
Activity after 4 half lives: 1000 ÷ 2 = 500,
Activity after 5 half lives: 500 ÷ 2 = 250.
So it takes **5 half-lives** to drop to 250 Bq
[2 marks for correct answer, otherwise 1 mark for attempting to halve values to find number of half-lives]

c) (100 ÷ 8000) × 100 *[1 mark]* = **1.25%** *[1 mark]*

Section 5 — Forces and Energy

Page 87

Warm-Up Questions

1 A system is the object or group of objects that you are interested in.

2 true

3 Energy is transferred electrically from the chemical energy store of the battery to the kinetic energy store of the fan's blades.

4 work done = force × distance moved in the direction of the force / $E = F \times d$

5 true

6 watts

Exam Questions

1 a) Energy is transferred from the ball's gravitational potential energy store *[1 mark]* to its kinetic energy store *[1 mark]*.

b) There will be no change in total energy *[1 mark]*.
In a closed system, the net change in energy is always zero.

2 a) i) power = work done ÷ time taken / $P = E \div t$ *[1 mark]*

ii) $P = 1000 \div 20$
= **50 W** *[1 mark]*

b) efficiency = useful energy transferred by the device ÷ total energy supplied to the device
efficiency = 480 ÷ 1000
= **0.48 (= 48%)**
[2 marks for correct answer, otherwise 1 mark for correct substitution]

c) It will be faster / complete the course in less time *[1 mark]* because the motor transfers the same amount of energy, but over a shorter time *[1 mark]*.

3 a) work done = force × distance moved in the direction of the force / $E = F \times d$
$E = 42\,000 \times 700$
= 29 400 000 J
= **29 400 kJ**
[3 marks for correct answer, otherwise 1 mark for correct substitution and 1 mark for correct answer in J]

b) $KE = \frac{1}{2} \times m \times v^2$

$v = \sqrt{\dfrac{2 \times KE}{m}}$

$= \sqrt{\dfrac{2 \times 29\,400\,000}{150\,000}}$ = **19.79... m/s = 20 m/s (to 1 s.f.)**

[3 marks for correct answer, otherwise 1 mark for correct rearrangement and 1 mark for correct substitution]

Even if you got the answer to (a) wrong, you get full marks for (b) if you did the calculations correctly with your answer for (a).

Page 91

Warm-Up Questions

1 false
Non-contact forces occur between objects that aren't touching.

2 The relative magnitude of the forces.

3 A resultant force is the single force obtained by combining all the forces acting on an object. The resultant force has the same effect on the object as all the original forces together.

4 The tip of the last force you draw should end where the tail of the first force you drew began. E.g. for three forces the scale diagram will form a triangle.

Exam Questions

1 a) Total force to the right = 1700 + 300 = 2000 N
Total force to the left = 2000 N
Total horizontal force = 2000 – 2000 = 0 N
Resultant force = downwards force – upwards force
= 800 – 300
= **500 N downwards**
[3 marks for correct answer, otherwise 1 mark for correctly calculating that the total horizontal force is zero and 1 mark for giving the correct direction of the resultant force]

b) Total vertical force = 0 N
so, $y = $ **400 N**
Total horizontal force = 0 N
so, $x + 500$ N = 2000 N
$x = 2000 - 500 = $ **1500 N**
[2 marks — 1 mark for each correct answer]

2 a) i)

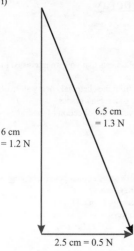

6 cm
= 1.2 N

6.5 cm
= 1.3 N

2.5 cm = 0.5 N

On the scale diagram the resultant force vector measures 6.5 cm.
6.5 ÷ 5 = 1.3 N
1.3 N (±0.02 N)
[3 marks for correct answer, otherwise 1 mark for drawing
forces tip-to-tail and 1 mark for drawing the vertical force
6 cm long and the horizontal force 2.5 cm long]
When creating a scale drawing, use a protractor to help you draw forces that are
at right angles.

ii) Using the scale drawing from a) i):

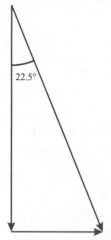

22.5°

22.5° (±1°) *[1 mark]*
b) E.g. electrostatic / magnetic *[1 mark]*.

Section 6 — Electricity and Circuits

Page 99
Warm-Up Questions

1

2 ohms
3 false
Current in metals is the flow of free electrons.
4 energy transferred = charge moved × potential difference / $E = Q × V$
5 Electrons collide with the ions in the lattice that make up the resistor
   as they flow through it. These collisions transfer energy to the kinetic
   energy store of the ions, causing them to vibrate more (so the energy in
   the thermal energy store of the resistor will increase).
6 In parallel with the component.
7

8 It decreases.

1 a) i) $Q = I × t$
            $= 0.30 × 35$
            $= \textbf{10.5 C}$
            [2 marks for correct answer, otherwise 1 mark for correct substitution]
       ii) $E = Q × V$
            $= 10.5 × 1.5$
            $= \textbf{15.75 J}$
            $= \textbf{16 J (to 2 s.f.)}$
            [2 marks for correct answer, otherwise 1 mark for correct substitution]
If you got the answer to (i) wrong, you still get full marks for (ii) if you did the calculations
correctly using your answer to (i).
   b)   It will decrease *[1 mark]*.
2 a)   The temperature of the circuit/diode *[1 mark]*.
   b)   At point A, $V = 6$ V, $I = 3$ A
            potential difference = current × resistance / $V = I × R$
            $R = V ÷ I$
            $= 6 ÷ 3$
            $= \textbf{2 Ω}$
            [4 marks for correct answer, otherwise 1 mark for obtaining correct
            values from the graph, 1 mark for correct rearrangement and 1 mark
            for correct substitution]

Page 103
Warm-Up Questions
1   true
2   The resistances of all the components are added together.
3   3 V
In a parallel circuit all of the components get the full source potential difference.
4   Two resistors connected in series.
5   One by one, connect identical resistors in series. Each time a new
        resistor is added, measure the current passing through the circuit using
        an ammeter, and then calculate the total resistance using $R = V ÷ I$, where
        V is the potential difference of the power supply. Plot a graph of total
        resistance against number of resistors.

1 a)   total resistance = $R_1 + R_2 + R_3$
            $= 2 + 3 + 5$
            $= \textbf{10 Ω} \textit{[1 mark]}$
   b)   The reading on A_2 will be 0.4 A *[1 mark]* because in a series circuit, the
            same current flows through all parts of the circuit *[1 mark]*.
   c) $V_3 = V_{supply} - V_1 - V_2$
            $= 4 - 0.8 - 1.2$
            $= \textbf{2 V} \textit{[1 mark]}$
2 a)   **15 V** *[1 mark]*
Potential difference is the same across each branch in a parallel circuit.
   b) $V = I × R$
            $I = V ÷ R$
            $= 15 ÷ 3$
            $= \textbf{5 A}$
            [3 marks for correct answer, otherwise 1 mark for correct
            rearrangement and 1 mark for correct substitution]
   c) $I_2 = 5 + 3.75$
            $= \textbf{8.75 A} \textit{[1 mark]}$
Even if you got the answer to (b) wrong, you still get full marks for (c) if you did the
calculations correctly with your answer to (b).
   d)   The reading on A_2 will decrease *[1 mark]* since current through the
            branch with two resistors will decrease *[1 mark]*, decreasing the total
            current in the circuit *[1 mark]*.

Page 107
Warm-Up Questions
1   energy transferred = current × potential difference × time / $E = I × V × t$
2   Energy is transferred electrically from the mains supply to the thermal
        energy store of the toaster's heating element.
3   E.g. electric heaters/toasters
4   watts
5   The 60 W light bulb.
6       $P = I^2 × R$

Exam Questions
1 a)   electrical power = current × potential difference / $P = I × V$ *[1 mark]*
   b) $I = P ÷ V$
            $= (2.8 × 1000) ÷ 230$
            $= \textbf{12.17... A}$
            $= \textbf{12 A (to 2 s.f.)}$
            [3 marks for correct answer, otherwise 1 mark for correct
            rearrangement and 1 mark for correct substitution]
   c)   She should choose kettle B because it has the higher power rating
            [1 mark]. This means that it transfers more energy to heat the water per
            unit time, so it will boil the water faster *[1 mark]*.

2 a) $E = I \times V \times t$

$t = 0.5$ hours $= 30$ minutes

Convert minutes into seconds: $30 \times 60 = 1800$ s

$E = 0.5 \times 3.0 \times 1800$

    $= \textbf{2700 J}$

[3 marks for correct answer, otherwise 1 mark for correctly converting time into seconds and 1 mark for correct substitution]

b) The power of the torch will be halved *[1 mark]*

The current has been halved, and as $P = I \times V$, halving the current and keeping the potential difference the same means the power will also be halved.

3 Calculate the lifetime of a single battery:

$E = I \times V \times t$

$t = \dfrac{E}{I \times V}$

    $= \dfrac{13\,000}{(0.2 \times 10^{-3}) \times 1.5} = 4.333... \times 10^7$ s

Then calculate the number of batteries required for ten years:

    $= \dfrac{\text{ten years (seconds)}}{\text{lifetime of one battery (seconds)}}$

    $= \dfrac{10 \times 365 \times 24 \times 60 \times 60}{4.333... \times 10^7} = 7.2775...$ batteries

So **8 batteries** are needed to power the clock for ten years.

[3 marks for correct answer, otherwise 1 mark for correctly calculating the lifetime of a single battery and 1 mark for dividing the number of seconds in ten years by the lifetime of a single battery]

Alternative method:

Number of seconds in ten years $= 10 \times 365 \times 24 \times 60 \times 60$

    $= 315\,360\,000$ s

Calculate the energy required by the clock in ten years:

$E = I \times V \times t$

    $= (0.2 \times 10^{-3}) \times 1.5 \times 315\,360\,000$

    $= 94\,608$ J

Then calculate the total number of batteries needed to supply this amount of energy:

Number of batteries $= 94\,608 \div 13\,000$

    $= 7.2775...$

So **8 batteries** are needed to power the clock for ten years.

[3 marks for correct answer, otherwise 1 mark for correctly calculating the total energy required for ten years and 1 mark for dividing this by the energy of a single battery]

Page 111

Warm-Up Questions

1 direct current
2 The neutral wire completes the circuit, allowing current to flow out of the appliance.
3 230 V
4 the live wire
5 false

Fuses should be rated as near as possible but just higher than the normal operating current.

Exam Questions

1 a) In alternating current the movement of charges constantly changes direction *[1 mark]*.
b) Your body is at 0 V, so there's a potential difference of around 230 V between the live wire and you *[1 mark]*. Touching the wire forms a link from the supply to the earth through your body *[1 mark]*, causing a large current to flow through you, which is an electric shock *[1 mark]*.
2 a) The earth wire is connected to the kettle's metal casing *[1 mark]*. When the casing becomes live, a large current is able to surge from the live wire, through the casing and out through the earth wire *[1 mark]*. The surge in current causes the fuse attached to the live wire to melt, isolating the kettle from the live supply *[1 mark]*.
b) a circuit breaker *[1 mark]*
c) Because plastic is a good electrical insulator, the casing cannot become live, so an earth wire is not needed *[1 mark]*.

Section 7 — Magnetic Fields

Page 118

Warm-Up Questions

1 a) attraction

Opposite poles are facing each other and opposite poles attract.

b)

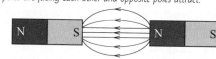

The magnetic field is uniform between the two bar magnets, so you need to draw at least 3 parallel field lines that are equally spaced.

2 Put the magnet on a piece of paper and put a compass next to it. Make a mark on the paper at each end of the compass needle. Then move the compass so that the tail of the compass needle is where the tip of the needle was previously, and mark again where the needle is pointing. Repeat this several times and then join up the markings for a complete sketch of a field line around the magnet. Do this several times for different points around the magnet to get several field lines. Add arrows to each field line, pointing from north to south.
3 north/towards the Earth's North Pole
4 false

A permanent magnet will always attract an induced magnet/magnetic material.

Exam Questions

1 a)

    [1 mark]

b) The interaction between the magnetic field generated by the wire and the magnetic field between the north and south poles of the bar magnets *[1 mark]*.

c) $l = 7.0$ cm $= 0.070$ m

$F = B \times I \times l$

    $= 0.028 \times 5.5 \times 0.070$

    $= \textbf{0.01078 N} = \textbf{0.011 N (to 2 s.f.)}$

[2 marks for correct answer, otherwise 1 mark for correct substitution]

d) The direction of the force would be reversed *[1 mark]*.

2 a) The field lines inside each loop of the solenoid all point in the same direction, so they add together to create a strong uniform field *[1 mark]*.

b) e.g. iron / nickel / cobalt *[1 mark]*

c) E.g. increase the current flowing through the solenoid *[1 mark]*.

Page 121

Warm-Up Questions

1 The induction of a potential difference in a conductor which is experiencing a changing magnetic field.
2 true
3 More turns on the secondary coil.
4 Because the high current would result in inefficient transmission of power/a large loss of energy to thermal energy stores.

Exam Questions

1 a) The coil experiences a change in magnetic field, so a potential difference is induced *[1 mark]*.
b) Any one from: e.g. move the magnet out of the coil / move the coil away from the magnet / insert the south pole of the magnet into the same end of the coil / insert the north pole of the magnet into the other end of the coil *[1 mark]*.
c) Any one from: e.g. push the magnet into the coil more quickly / use a stronger magnet / add more turns per unit length of wire *[1 mark]*.
d) Zero / no reading *[1 mark]*.

A moving/changing magnetic field is needed to generate a potential difference.

2 a) Step-up transformers are used at power stations to increase the potential difference (and so decrease the current) of the electricity produced for efficient transmission *[1 mark]*. Step-down transformers at the consumers' end reduce the potential difference to safe levels that can be used by consumers *[1 mark]*.

b) An alternating current in the primary coil produces an alternating magnetic field *[1 mark]*. This causes an alternating magnetic field in the iron core and through the secondary coil. The changing magnetic field through the secondary coil induces a potential difference in the secondary coil *[1 mark]*.

3 $V_p \times I_p = V_s \times I_s$

$I_s = \dfrac{V_p \times I_p}{V_s} = \dfrac{12 \times 2.5}{4}$

$I_s = \textbf{7.5 A}$

[2 marks for correct answer, otherwise 1 mark for correct substitution]

Section 8 — Matter

Page 127

Warm-Up Questions

1 Density is a measure of the amount of mass in a given volume / compactness of a substance.
2 gas
3 sublimation
4 physical changes
5 Cooling a system decreases its internal energy.
6 -273 °C
7 The higher the temperature of the gas, the faster the gas particles move. This means the gas particles collide with the walls of the container more often and with a greater force. This causes the gas pressure to increase.

Exam Questions

1 a) Particles are held close together in a fixed, regular pattern *[1 mark]*. They vibrate about fixed positions *[1 mark]*.

b) density = mass ÷ volume
= 850.5 ÷ 75.0
= **11.34 g/cm³**
[2 marks for correct answer, otherwise 1 mark for correct substitution]

c) melting *[1 mark]*

2 a) C *[1 mark]*.

b) The volume of the toy soldier / the volume of water displaced by the toy soldier *[1 mark]*. The mass of the toy soldier *[1 mark]*.

c) How to grade your answer:

Level 0: There is no relevant information. *[No marks]*

Level 1: There is a brief description of an experiment to measure the density of the toy soldier, but the answer isn't very clear. The points made do not link together. *[1 to 2 marks]*

Level 2: There is a description of an experiment to measure the mass and volume of the toy soldier, with reference to the equipment needed. The answer has some structure. *[3 to 4 marks]*

Level 3: There is a clear and detailed description of an experiment to measure the density of the toy soldier. The method includes details of how to use the equipment and how to process the results to work out the density of the toy soldier. The answer is well structured. *[5 to 6 marks]*

Here are some points your answer may include:
Measure and record the mass of the toy soldier using the mass balance.
Fill a eureka can with water.
Place an empty measuring cylinder beneath the spout of the eureka can.
Submerge the toy soldier in the eureka can.
Measure the volume of water displaced from the eureka can using the measuring cylinder.
The volume of water displaced is equal to the volume of the soldier.
Use the equation density = mass ÷ volume / $\rho = m \div V$ to calculate the density of the toy soldier.

With questions where you have to describe a method, make sure your description is clear and detailed.

Page 131
Warm-Up Questions

1 The change in energy in the substance's thermal energy store needed to raise the temperature of 1 kg of that substance by 1 °C.

2 J/kg

3 The thermally insulating material reduces unwanted energy transfers to the surroundings. More of the energy supplied is transferred to the thermal energy stores of the water, so the ΔE value used to calculate the specific heat capacity is a more accurate value. This improves the accuracy of the value of specific heat capacity.

4

Exam Questions

1 $Q = m \times L$
So, $L = Q \div m$
$m = 40.8$ g = (40.8 ÷ 1000) kg = 0.0408 kg
$L = 47\,100 \div 0.0408 =$ **1.1544... × 10⁶ J/kg**
= **1.15 × 10⁶ J/kg (to 3 s.f.)**
[2 marks for correct answer, otherwise 1 mark for correct substitution]

2 a) $\Delta Q = m \times c \times \Delta\theta$
So, $c = \Delta Q \div (m \times \Delta\theta)$
$\Delta\theta = 100 - 20 = 80$ °C
$c = 36\,000 \div (0.5 \times 80)$
= **900 J/kg°C**
[2 marks for correct answer, otherwise 1 mark for correct substitution]

b) Concrete has a higher specific heat capacity *[1 mark]* and so will be able to store a lot more energy in its thermal energy store for the same temperature change, and therefore emit a lot more energy during the day *[1 mark]*. This means it will be able to heat the room to a higher temperature / for longer *[1 mark]*.

3 a) In the graph, $y = \Delta\theta$ and $x = \Delta Q$.
$\Delta Q = m \times c \times \Delta\theta$
Rearrange this equation to make it look like $y = mx + c$:
$\Delta\theta = \dfrac{1}{m \times c} \times \Delta Q$
Comparing this to $y = mx + c$,
the gradient of the graph must equal $\dfrac{1}{m \times c}$ *[1 mark]*
Coordinates of two points on the line of best fit are (0,0) and (3000, 0.70), where x has been converted from kJ to J.
Gradient = $\Delta y \div \Delta x = (0.70 - 0) \div (3000 - 0)$
= 0.0002333... *[1 mark]*
$c = \dfrac{1}{m \times \text{gradient}}$
$m = 1.0$ kg, so $c = \dfrac{1}{1 \times 0.0002333...}$ = **4285.71... J/kg °C**
= **4300 J/kg °C (to 2 s.f.)** *[1 mark]*

b) Lower — in the investigation, some of the energy transferred by the heater would have been transferred to the thermal energy stores of the surroundings rather than the water *[1 mark]*. For the same temperature change to have occurred for a smaller amount of energy transferred, the specific heat capacity must be smaller *[1 mark]*.

Page 135
Warm-Up Questions

1 false
In order to distort a spring, at least two forces must be applied to the spring.

2 An object undergoing elastic distortion will go back to its original shape and length after the distorting forces have been removed.

3 force = spring constant × extension / $F = k \times x$

Exam Questions

1 extension = 4 cm = 0.04 m
work done = area under graph
= ½ × 8 × 0.04
= **0.16 J**
[2 marks for correct answer, otherwise 1 mark for attempting to find the area under the graph]

2 a) The mass on the bottom of the spring / the force applied to the bottom of the spring *[1 mark]*.

b) Any one from: e.g. the spring used throughout the experiment / the temperature the experiment is carried out at *[1 mark]*.

c) extension = 2.5 cm = 0.025 m
$F = k \times x$
so $k = F \div x$
= 4 ÷ 0.025
= **160 N/m**
[3 marks for correct answer, otherwise 1 mark for correct rearrangement and 1 mark for correct substitution]

Remember to convert the measurement of extension from cm into m before you do your calculation.

d) The spring has been inelastically distorted *[1 mark]*.

3 $E = ½ \times k \times x^2$
Rearrange for x:
$x = \sqrt{\dfrac{2 \times E}{k}} = \sqrt{\dfrac{2 \times 36}{400}}$ = 0.42426... m
So length of spring after compression = 1.20 − 0.42426...
= **0.77573... m**
= **0.78 m (to 2 s.f.)**
[3 marks for correct answer, otherwise 1 mark for correct substitution and 1 mark for calculating compression = 0.42426... m]

Practice Paper 1
Pages 141-154

1 a) i) E.g. total energy must be conserved / energy cannot be created or destroyed, only transferred. *[1 mark]*
ii) C *[1 mark]*
iii) C *[1 mark]*

b) i) E.g. measure the temperature after a set number of bounces instead of after a set time *[1 mark]*.
This is a sensible idea as the number of bounces in a given time may vary.

ii) E.g. energy is transferred mechanically from the ball's kinetic energy store *[1 mark]* to its elastic potential energy store as it hits the wall and deforms *[1 mark]*. Some energy is transferred by heating to the thermal energy store of the ball *[1 mark]*. Energy is transferred mechanically from the elastic potential energy store of the ball to the kinetic energy store of the ball as the ball rebounds from the wall *[1 mark]*.

c) change in GPE = 0.03 × 10 × 1.75
= **0.525 J**
[2 marks for correct answer, otherwise 1 mark for correct substitution]

2 a) i) E.g. biofuel / wind power / hydroelectricity / the tides *[1 mark]*
   ii) Efficiency = useful energy transferred by the device ÷
      total energy transferred to the device. *[1 mark]*
   iii) Efficiency = useful energy transferred by the device ÷
      total energy transferred to the device
      = 0.2 ÷ 1.2
      = **0.1666...**
      = **0.17 (= 17%) (to 2 s.f.)**
      [2 marks for correct answer, otherwise 1 mark for correct substitution]
  b) i) The amount of energy used has decreased over time
      [1 mark]. E.g. this could be because electrical devices
      have become more efficient over time *[1 mark]*.
   ii) Any two from: e.g. building renewable power plants is expensive /
      using fossil fuels is fairly cheap / some people don't want to live near
      renewable power plants / renewable energy resources are not as reliable
      as fossil fuels / research into improving the reliability and reducing the
      cost of renewable resources is expensive and time consuming / making
      personal changes (such as installing solar panels) can be expensive
      for an individual *[2 marks — 1 mark for each correct point]*.
  c) The home owner should use brick Y *[1 mark]*, because brick Y has the
      lowest thermal conductivity of all the options. This means the rate of
      energy transfer by heating will be slowest through this type of brick
      [1 mark]. Also brick Y is the thickest brick and the thicker the walls of a
      building, the lower the rate of cooling of the building will be *[1 mark]*.

3 a) The woman travels at a constant speed for the first 15 s
      (travelling 33 m) *[1 mark]*. She then remains stationary
      (at 33 m) for 10 s *[1 mark]* before accelerating away for
      the next 10 s (and travelling another 12 m) *[1 mark]*.
  b) The gradient of the line between 0 s and 15 s will give speed.
      $$\text{speed = gradient} = \frac{\text{change in } y}{\text{change in } x}$$
      $$= \frac{33 - 0}{15 - 0}$$
      $$= \textbf{2.2 m/s}$$
      *[2 marks for correct answer, otherwise 1 mark for correct
      method for calculating speed from the graph]*
  c) i) Speed = distance ÷ time *[1 mark]*
   ii) Time = distance ÷ speed
      = 14 ÷ 3.5
      = **4 s**
      *[3 marks for the correct answer, otherwise 1 mark for correct
      rearrangement and 1 mark for correct substitution]*
  d) i) A *[1 mark]*
   ii) The total frictional force must be larger than
      the total driving forces *[1 mark]*.

4 a) E.g. place a block on a sheet of paper and draw around it. Shine a light
      beam through the block *[1 mark]*. Trace the path of the ray using a pencil
      and a ruler. Measure and record the angles of incidence and refraction
      [1 mark]. Repeat this for different materials, keeping the angle of
      incidence the same *[1 mark]*.
  b) i) e.g. ray box *[1 mark]*
   ii) E.g. it allows the centre of the beam to be traced more
      accurately, meaning better angle measurements *[1 mark]*.
  c) i) Flint glass *[1 mark]*
   ii) Flint glass refracts the light beam by the greatest amount *[1 mark]* and
      refraction is caused by light being slowed down by a material *[1 mark]*.
  d) $v = f \times \lambda$
      $= (5.1 \times 10^{14}) \times (353 \times 10^{-9})$
      $= 1.800... \times 10^8$
      $= \textbf{1.8} \times \textbf{10}^8$ **m/s (to 2 s.f.)**
      [2 marks for correct answer, otherwise 1 mark for correct substitution]

5 a) How to grade your answer:
   Level 0: There is no relevant information. *[No marks]*
   Level 1: There is a brief description of both models of the atom.
             The points made do not link together. *[1 to 2 marks]*
   Level 2: There is a description of both models of the atom,
             and some description of the scientific discoveries
             that led to the development of the nuclear model.
             The answer has some structure. *[3 to 4 marks]*
   Level 3: There is a clear and detailed description of both models
             of the atom, and of the scientific discoveries and
             experiments which led to the development of the nuclear
             model. The answer is well structured. *[5 to 6 marks]*
   Here are some points your answer may include:
   Model X is the plum pudding model of the atom.
   The plum pudding model describes the atom as a sphere of positive
   charge, with negatively charged electrons within it.
   Model Y is the nuclear/Bohr model of the atom.
   The nuclear/Bohr model of the atom describes the atom as a nucleus,
   made up of positively charged protons and uncharged neutrons, orbited
   by electrons.
   In the early 20th century (1909), Rutherford and Marsden performed the
   alpha scattering experiment.

They fired a beam of positively charged alpha particles at a thin gold foil.
Based on the plum pudding model, they expected all the alpha particles to
pass through the foil, with some deflection.
However, they found that most alpha particles passed through the foil
without deflecting, while a small few were deflected back towards the
emitter.
This suggested that most of the atom is empty space, since so many of the
alpha particles passed through without deflecting.
It also suggested there was a small, positively charged 'nucleus' in the
centre of the atom, which caused the backwards deflection of the alpha
particles.
Later, Bohr proposed that the electrons in an atom could
only be found in fixed orbits named energy levels.
  b) i) E.g. a Geiger-Müller tube *[1 mark]*
   ii) The charge on a beta particle, B = −1
      83 = A − 1
      A = **84** *[1 mark]*
   iii) The initial count-rate was 80 cps.
      80 ÷ 2 = 40
      So after one half-life, the count-rate will be 40 cps.
      From the graph, 40 cps is reached after 60 minutes.
      So half-life = **60 minutes**.
      *[2 marks for correct answer, otherwise 1 mark for correct
      method of calculating half-life graphically]*
  c) A thicker lead lining blocks more gamma radiation *[1 mark]*,
      which improves the safety of people nearby since gamma
      radiation can damage or kill cells *[1 mark]*.

6 a) 10 dB *[1 mark]*
  b) wavelength = 2 × 0.625 = 1.25 m
      wave speed = frequency × wavelength
      = 5500 × 1.25
      = 6875 m/s
      = **6900 m/s (to 2 s.f.)**
      *[4 marks for correct answer, otherwise 1 mark for correctly
      calculating wavelength, 1 mark for correct substitution
      and 1 mark for correct unrounded answer]*
  c) A *[1 mark]*

Practice Paper 2
Pages 155-169

1 a) i) A *[1 mark]*
   ii) time = charge ÷ current = 1440 ÷ 12 = **120 s**
      *[3 marks for correct answer, otherwise 1 mark for correct
      rearrangement and 1 mark for correct substitution]*
  b) E.g. the maximum safe power that an appliance can
      operate at / the maximum amount of energy an appliance
      can transfer between stores per second *[1 mark]*.
  c) Energy is transferred from the thermal energy store
      of the heating element *[1 mark]* to the thermal energy
      store of the water *[1 mark]* by heating *[1 mark]*.
  d) E.g.

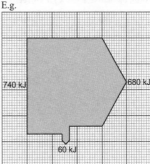

740 kJ   680 kJ

60 kJ

*[2 marks for a correctly drawn diagram, otherwise 1 mark for
correct width of one arrow or correct calculation of waste energy]*

2 a) i) B *[1 mark]*
   *The clamp must apply 1 N of force to balance the weight of the mass. Otherwise, there
   will be a resultant force on the spring causing it to move.*
   ii) If only one force was applied, this would simply cause the
      spring to move in the direction of the force *[1 mark]*.
  b) D *[1 mark]*

c) How to grade your answer:
Level 0: There is no relevant information. *[No marks]*
Level 1: There is a brief description of an experiment using the equipment shown. The points made are not linked together. *[1 to 2 marks]*
Level 2: There is a description of an experiment that can be performed with the equipment shown, and a valid statement of how to calculate the spring constant. The answer has some structure. *[3 to 4 marks]*
Level 3: There is a clear and detailed description of an experiment that can be performed using the equipment shown, and of how to calculate the spring constant from the resulting force-extension graph. The answer is well structured. *[5 to 6 marks]*

Here are some points your answer may include:
Measure the mass of the masses that are to be hung from the spring using a mass balance.
Calculate the weight of each of the masses using $W = m \times g$.
Using the ruler, measure the length of the spring when it has no masses hanging from it (the unstretched length).
Hang a mass from the spring, and record the new length of the spring.
Calculate the extension of the spring by subtracting the unstretched length from the new length.
Increase the number of masses hanging from the spring in steps, recording the new weight and calculating the extension each time.
Once there are a suitable number of points, plot the results on a force-extension graph, with force on the y-axis, and extension on the x-axis.
Draw a line of best fit through the results.
Spring constant = force ÷ extension ($k = F \div e$).
So the spring constant can be calculated by finding the gradient of the linear part of the graph.

d) Work done is equal to area under the graph up to point A.
Extension = 3.0 cm = 0.030 m
Area = area of a triangle = ½ × base × height
$= \frac{1}{2} \times 0.030 \times 6.0$
$= \textbf{0.09 J}$
[3 marks for correct answer, otherwise 1 mark for correctly converting cm to m and 1 mark for a correct method of calculating the area under the graph]
You could have used the counting the squares method here instead if you had wanted to. Either method used correctly will get you full marks.

e) The rubber band did behave elastically, as it returned to its original shape and size once the forces acting on it were removed *[1 mark]*. However, the force-extension graph for the rubber band was a curve, so the relationship between force and extension was not linear *[1 mark]*.

3 a) C *[1 mark]*
b) 30 minutes = 30 × 60 = 1800 s
$Q = I \times t = 2.4 \times 1800 = \textbf{4320} = \textbf{4300 C (to 2 s.f.)}$
[2 marks for correct answer, otherwise 1 mark for correct substitution.]
c) $F = B \times I \times l$
$= 0.75 \times 2.4 \times 0.05 = \textbf{0.09 N}$
[2 marks for correct answer, otherwise 1 mark for correct substitution.]
d) Any one from: e.g. increase the current through the wire / increase the magnetic flux density/strength of the magnetic field / increase the length of the wire inside the magnetic field *[1 mark]*.

4 a) E.g.

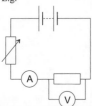

[1 mark for variable resistor, fixed resistor and ammeter drawn in series with the battery, 1 mark for voltmeter drawn in parallel to the fixed resistor, 1 mark for all circuit symbols drawn correctly]

b) mean $= \frac{2.53 + 2.52 + 2.51}{3} = \textbf{2.52 A}$ *[1 mark]*

c) E.g. when a current flows through the resistor, electrons collide with the ions in the lattice that make up the resistor *[1 mark]*. This gives energy to the ions, which makes them vibrate more (causing the resistor to heat up) *[1 mark]*.

d) $V = I \times R = 5 \times 2 = \textbf{10 V}$
[2 marks for correct answer, otherwise 1 mark for correct substitution]

e) D *[1 mark]*

5 a) i) E.g. wear insulated gloves to move the container / don't move the container until it is cool / keep all electronics (apart from the immersion heater) away from the water *[1 mark]*
ii) E.g. joulemeter *[1 mark]*
b) Comparing $y = mx + c$ and $Q = m \times L$, with Q on the y-axis and m on the x-axis, you can see that the gradient of the graph is equal to L.
Gradient = change in y ÷ change in x
$= 0.34 \div 0.15 = 2.266... = \textbf{2.3 MJ/kg (to 2 s.f.)}$
(accept between 2.2 and 2.3 MJ/kg)
[2 marks for correct answer, otherwise 1 mark for correct method for calculating the gradient of the graph]
c) A *[1 mark]*
Reading from the graph, 0.42 MJ of energy was required to boil off 0.185 kg of water.
$E = IVt$, so $t = \frac{E}{IV} = \frac{0.42 \times 10^6}{8 \times 12} = 4375$ s.
d) E.g. particles of liquid water are closer together than particles of water vapour. / Particles of liquid water have less energy in their kinetic stores/move slower than particles of water vapour *[1 mark]*.

6 a) i) electrical power = current × potential difference / $P = I \times V$ *[1 mark]*
ii) Potential difference across the motor = 12.0 – 4.0 = 8.0 V
Current through the motor = 5.0 – 3.0 = 2.0 A
$P = I \times V = 2.0 \times 8.0 = \textbf{16 W}$
[3 marks for correct answer, otherwise 1 mark for correct calculation of potential difference across the motor or current through the motor and 1 mark for correct substitution into the power equation.]
b) i) The motors transfer energy to the kinetic energy store of the fan blades *[1 mark]*. Power is the rate of energy transfer, so using a more powerful motor will cause the fan blades to increase their speed at a higher rate / reach a higher maximum speed *[1 mark]*. So motor A has the highest power *[1 mark]*.
ii) E.g. lubricate the motors *[1 mark]*.
c) As the temperature increases, the resistance of the thermistor will decrease *[1 mark]*, so the potential difference across the thermistor will decrease *[1 mark]*. As the thermistor is in parallel with the heater, the potential difference across the heater will decrease *[1 mark]*.
d) Energy usefully transferred = $\Delta Q = m \times c \times \Delta\theta$
$\Delta\theta = 65 - 16 = 49 \text{ °C}$
$\Delta Q = 2.1 \times 4200 \times 49 = 432\,180$ J
Total useful energy transferred by device = 432 180 J
efficiency $= \frac{\text{useful energy transferred by device}}{\text{total energy supplied to device}}$
total energy supplied to device
= useful energy transferred by device ÷ efficiency
= 432 180 ÷ 0.85
$= \textbf{508 447.058... J} = \textbf{510 000 J (to 2 s.f.)}$
[4 marks for correct answer, otherwise 1 mark for correct substitution to find energy usefully transferred, 1 mark for correct rearrangement of efficiency equation and 1 mark for correct substitution into rearranged efficiency equation]

Index

Index